HIGHER SCORES ON

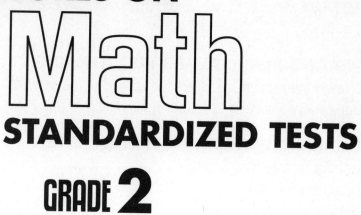

STANDARDIZED TESTS

GRADE 2

Contents

Introduction

Welcome to *Higher Scores on Math Standardized Tests*, Grade 2. You have selected a book that will help your child develop the skills he or she needs to succeed on the standardized math tests. The items in this workbook have been closely aligned to the Common Core State Standards for Mathematics, which cover grade-level skills for mathematics.

Although testing can be a source of anxiety for children, this book will give your child the preparation and practice that he or she needs to feel better prepared and more confident when taking standardized math tests. Research shows that children who are acquainted with the scoring format of standardized tests score higher on those tests. Students also score higher when they practice and understand the skills and objectives covered on the tests.

This book has many features that will help you prepare your child to take standardized math tests:
- Modeled instruction about how to answer test questions and hints to guide the child toward the correct response
- Test-taking tips
- Pretest and Practice Tests in a standardized test format
- A complete answer key, including references to the specific Common Core State Standards being tested
- A correlation of the Common Core State Standards to the questions

If your child expresses anxiety about taking a test or completing these lessons, help him or her understand what causes the stress. Then, talk about ways to eliminate anxiety. Above all, enjoy this time you spend with your child. He or she will feel your support, and test scores will improve as success in test taking is experienced. Help your child maintain a positive attitude about taking a standardized test. Let him or her know that each test provides an opportunity to shine.

Multiple-Choice Items

Multiple-choice items will be familiar to children from other experiences. For multiple-choice items, four answer choices are given. The item itself may be a multi-step problem.

To help children succeed with multiple-choice items:

- Have children solve the problem first.
- Have children find the answer choice that matches their solution.
- Once the correct answer has been identified, demonstrate how to mark the answer.

What if no answer matches?

- Have children consider that Not Here may be the correct answer.
- Have children restate the problem in their own words to determine the source of the error.
- Have children evaluate each answer choice to eliminate ones that do not fit the problem.
- Have volunteers demonstrate how they solved multiple-choice problems.

Common Core State Standards for Mathematics Correlation Chart

Standard	Descriptor	Pretest	Lessons	Practice Test A	Practice Test B
	Operations and Algebraic Thinking				
	Represent and solve problems involving addition and subtraction.				
2.OA.1	Use addition and subtraction within 100 to solve one- and two-step word problems involving situations of adding to, taking from, putting together, taking apart, and comparing, with unknowns in all positions, e.g., by using drawings and equations with a symbol for the unknown number to represent the problem.	1–4	1–10, 25–46	2, 9, 25, 33	2, 9, 25, 33
	Add and subtract within 20.				
2.OA.2	Fluently add and subtract within 20 using mental strategies. By end of Grade 2, know from memory all sums of two one-digit numbers.	5–8	11–16, 47–60	10, 11, 35, 45	10, 11, 35, 45
	Work with equal groups of objects to gain foundations for multiplication.				
2.OA.3	Determine whether a group of objects (up to 20) has an odd or even number of members, e.g., by pairing objects or counting them by 2s; write an equation to express an even number as a sum of two equal addends.	9–11	17–21, 61–70	16, 26, 50	16, 26, 50
2.OA.4	Use addition to find the total number of objects arranged in rectangular arrays with up to 5 rows and up to 5 columns; write an equation to express the total as a sum of equal addends.	12–14	22–24, 71–78	32, 40, 43	32, 40, 43
	Number and Operations in Base Ten				
	Understand place value.				
2.NBT.1	Understand that the three digits of a three-digit number represent amounts of hundreds, tens, and ones; e.g., 706 equals 7 hundreds, 0 tens, and 6 ones. Understand the following as special cases:	15	1–2, 21–24	24	24
2.NBT.1.a	100 can be thought of as a bundle of ten tens — called a "hundred."	16	3, 25–26	39	39

Correlation Chart
Higher Scores on Math, Grade 2

Standard	Descriptor	Pretest	Lessons	Practice Test A	Practice Test B
2.NBT.1.b	The numbers 100, 200, 300, 400, 500, 600, 700, 800, 900 refer to one, two, three, four, five, six, seven, eight, or nine hundreds (and 0 tens and 0 ones).	17	4, 27–28	27	27
2.NBT.2	Count within 1000; skip-count by 5s, 10s, and 100s.	18	5–6, 29–32	21	21
2.NBT.3	Read and write numbers to 1000 using base-ten numerals, number names, and expanded form.	19–20	7–8, 33–36	3, 13	3, 13
2.NBT.4	Compare two three-digit numbers based on meanings of the hundreds, tens, and ones digits, using >, =, and < symbols to record the results of comparisons.	21	9–10, 37–40	41	41
	Use place value understanding and properties of operations to add and subtract.				
2.NBT.5	Fluently add and subtract within 100 using strategies based on place value, properties of operations, and/or the relationship between addition and subtraction.	22–23	11–13, 41–47	15, 31	15, 31
2.NBT.6	Add up to four two-digit numbers using strategies based on place value and properties of operations.	24–25	14–15, 48–51	34, 47	34, 47
2.NBT.7	Add and subtract within 1000, using concrete models or drawings and strategies based on place value, properties of operations, and/or the relationship between addition and subtraction; relate the strategy to a written method. Understand that in adding or subtracting three-digit numbers, one adds or subtracts hundreds and hundreds, tens and tens, ones and ones; and sometimes it is necessary to compose or decompose tens or hundreds.	26	16–17, 52–57	19	19
2.NBT.8	Mentally add 10 or 100 to a given number 100–900, and mentally subtract 10 or 100 from a given number 100–900.	27	18–19, 58–60	4	4
2.NBT.9	Explain why addition and subtraction strategies work, using place value and the properties of operations.	28	20, 61–62	14	14

Standard	Descriptor	Pretest	Lessons	Practice Test A	Practice Test B
	Measurement and Data				
	Measure and estimate lengths in standard units.				
2.MD.1	Measure the length of an object by selecting and using appropriate tools such as rulers, yardsticks, meter sticks, and measuring tapes.	29–30	1–2, 21–25	5, 36	5, 36
2.MD.2	Measure the length of an object twice, using length units of different lengths for the two measurements; describe how the two measurements relate to the size of the unit chosen.	31	3–4, 26–28	12	12
2.MD.3	Estimate lengths using units of inches, feet, centimeters, and meters.	32	5–6, 29–32	20	20
2.MD.4	Measure to determine how much longer one object is than another, expressing the length difference in terms of a standard length unit.	33	7, 33–34	37	37
	Relate addition and subtraction to length.				
2.MD.5	Use addition and subtraction within 100 to solve word problems involving lengths that are given in the same units, e.g., by using drawings (such as drawings of rulers) and equations with a symbol for the unknown number to represent the problem.	34–35	8–9, 35–38	7, 46	7, 46
2.MD.6	Represent whole numbers as lengths from 0 on a number line diagram with equally spaced points corresponding to the numbers 0, 1, 2, ..., and represent whole-number sums and differences within 100 on a number line diagram.	36	10–11, 39–42	28	28
	Work with time and money.				
2.MD.7	Tell and write time from analog and digital clocks to the nearest five minutes, using a.m. and p.m.	37–38	12–13, 43–46	17, 44	17, 44
2.MD.8	Solve word problems involving dollar bills, quarters, dimes, nickels, and pennies, using $ and ¢ symbols appropriately. Example: If you have 2 dimes and 3 pennies, how many cents do you have?	39–40	14–15, 47–51	29, 42	29, 42

Standard	Descriptor	Pretest	Lessons	Practice Test A	Practice Test B
	Represent and interpret data.				
2.MD.9	Generate measurement data by measuring lengths of several objects to the nearest whole unit, or by making repeated measurements of the same object. Show the measurements by making a line plot, where the horizontal scale is marked off in whole-number units.	41	16–17, 52–54	6	6
2.MD.10	Draw a picture graph and a bar graph (with single-unit scale) to represent a data set with up to four categories. Solve simple put-together, take-apart, and compare problems using information presented in a bar graph.	42	18–20, 55–57	23	23
	Geometry				
	Reason with shapes and their attributes.				
2.G.1	Recognize and draw shapes having specified attributes, such as a given number of angles or a given number of equal faces. Identify triangles, quadrilaterals, pentagons, hexagons, and cubes.	43–45	1–3, 9–17	30, 38, 48	30, 38, 48
2.G.2	Partition a rectangle into rows and columns of same-size squares and count to find the total number of them.	46–47	4–5, 18–23	22, 49	22, 49
2.G.3	Partition circles and rectangles into two, three, or four equal shares, describe the shares using the words halves, thirds, half of, a third of, etc., and describe the whole as two halves, three thirds, four fourths. Recognize that equal shares of identical wholes need not have the same shape.	48–50	6–8, 24–32	1, 8, 18	1, 8, 18

Name _____ Date _____

Pretest

DIRECTIONS: Read each question and choose the best answer. Fill in the circle for the answer you have chosen. If the correct answer is not available, mark the letter for "Not Here."

1. Declan rides his bicycle 24 miles one week. He rides 37 miles the next week. Which number sentence shows how to find the number of miles Declan rides in all?

   Ⓐ $24 + 37 = \square$

   Ⓑ $24 + \square = 37$

   Ⓒ $37 - 24 = \square$

   Ⓓ $37 - \square = 24$

2. Isabella buys 40 apples. She gives some apples away and has 32 left. How many apples does Isabella give away?

   Ⓕ 32

   Ⓖ 12

   Ⓗ 10

   Ⓙ 8

3. There are 9 brown rocks and 5 gray rocks in a box. If you take 7 rocks out of the box, how many rocks will be left?

   Ⓐ 5

   Ⓑ 7

   Ⓒ 14

   Ⓓ 21

4. Ozzi has 16 sports cards. If 4 of the cards are baseball cards, how many sports cards are NOT baseball cards?

   Ⓕ 20

   Ⓖ 16

   Ⓗ 12

   Ⓙ 2

5. Which number makes both of these sentences true?

$$3 + \square = 12$$
$$12 - 3 = \square$$

- (A) 15
- (B) 11
- (C) 9
- (D) 7

6. What is the missing number?

$$\square + 8 = 16$$

- (F) 7
- (G) 8
- (H) 9
- (J) 12

7. Which number sentence does NOT equal 14?

- (A) $15 - 1 = \square$
- (B) $10 + 4 = \square$
- (C) $9 + 5 = \square$
- (D) $9 - 5 = \square$

8. Find the difference.

$$\begin{array}{r} 18 \\ -\ 9 \\ \hline \end{array}$$

- (F) 9
- (G) 8
- (H) 7
- (J) Not Here

9. Which number sentence describes this group of rabbits as an odd number?

Ⓐ $6 = 3 + 3$

Ⓑ $7 = 3 + 3 + 1$

Ⓒ $8 = 4 + 4$

Ⓓ $9 = 4 + 4 + 1$

10. Which row of strawberries shows an even number?

Ⓕ

Ⓖ

Ⓗ

Ⓙ

11. Which pair of cube trains shows an odd number?

Ⓐ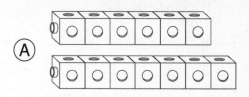

Ⓑ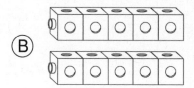

Ⓒ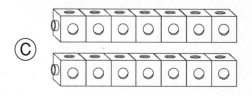

Ⓓ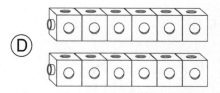

12. Which number sentence can you use to find the total number of ants?

Ⓕ $1 + 1 + 1 + 1 + 1 = 5$

Ⓖ $2 + 2 + 2 + 2 = 8$

Ⓗ $5 + 5 = 10$

Ⓙ $10 + 10 = 20$

13. Which number sentence shows how many squares are in this picture?

Ⓐ 2 + 2 + 2 = 6

Ⓑ 3 + 3 = 6

Ⓒ 3 + 3 + 3 = 9

Ⓓ 4 + 4 + 4 = 12

14. Hallie puts her stickers in 4 rows. There are 2 stickers in each row. Which addition sentence describes the number of stickers?

Ⓕ 2 + 2 + 2 = 6

Ⓖ 2 + 2 + 2 + 2 = 8

Ⓗ 4 + 4 + 4 = 12

Ⓙ Not Here

15. How many hundreds, tens, and ones are in 392?

Ⓐ 9 hundreds, 2 tens, 3 ones

Ⓑ 9 hundreds, 9 tens, 2 ones

Ⓒ 3 tens, 9 hundreds, 2 ones

Ⓓ 3 hundreds, 9 tens, 2 ones

16. The model shows groups of 10 tens. Which statement does the model prove?

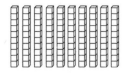
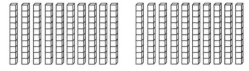

Ⓕ 30 tens = 3 hundreds

Ⓖ 30 tens = 30

Ⓗ 3 tens = 30 hundreds

Ⓙ 3 tens = 300

17. Look at the place-value model. What value does it show?

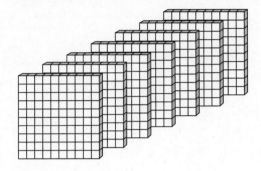

(A) 7 tens

(B) 7 ones

(C) 70

(D) 700

18. Count by tens. What number comes next?

130, 140, 150, ☐

(F) 151

(G) 155

(H) 160

(J) 250

19. Which number is seventy-three?

(A) 37

(B) 73

(C) 307

(D) 713

20. Which value is the same as two hundred forty-eight?

(F) 284

(G) 200 + 40 + 8

(H) 2 hundreds + 14 tens + 8 ones

(J) 200 hundreds, 40 tens, 8 ones

21. Compare the numbers. Which symbol belongs in the box?

918 ☐ 891

(A) <

(B) =

(C) >

(D) Not Here

22. Which number completes the math sentence?

$$40 + 30 = \square$$

Ⓕ 50

Ⓖ 60

Ⓗ 80

Ⓙ Not Here

23. Suki uses a calculator to add $78 + 13 = 91$. Which number sentence below can she also answer from this calculation?

Ⓐ $91 - 13 = \square$

Ⓑ $91 + 13 = \square$

Ⓒ $78 - 13 = \square$

Ⓓ $13 + 91 = \square$

24. Find the sum.

$$15 + 42 + 25 = \square$$

Ⓕ 82

Ⓖ 72

Ⓗ 67

Ⓙ 57

25. Find the sum.

$$\begin{array}{r} \square \\ 35 \\ 12 \\ 11 \\ + 32 \\ \hline \end{array}$$

Ⓐ 58

Ⓑ 78

Ⓒ 80

Ⓓ 90

Name _____ Date _____

26. Use a place-value chart to add 183 + 308. Regroup ones or tens if you need to. What is the sum?

Hundreds	Tens	Ones
□	□	
1	8	3
+ 3	0	8

F) 481

G) 485

H) 491

J) 591

27. Use mental math to add 526 + 100. What is the sum?

A) 426

B) 536

C) 626

D) 726

28. Gino uses place-value blocks to subtract 65 − 29. Why does he rename 65 as 5 tens and 15 ones?

F) There are not enough tens to subtract.

G) There are not enough ones to subtract.

H) He says there are 5 tens in 65.

J) Not Here

29. Use the inch ruler to measure. How long is the bookmark?

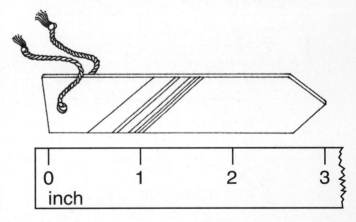

A) 3 inches

B) 2 inches

C) 1 inch

D) 0 inches

Pretest
Higher Scores on Math, Grade 2

30. A ladybug is shorter than an inch long. Which is the best tool for measuring the length of a ladybug?

Ⓕ yardstick

Ⓖ meter stick

Ⓗ inch ruler

Ⓙ centimeter ruler

31. Measure in centimeters and in inches. About how long is the leaf?

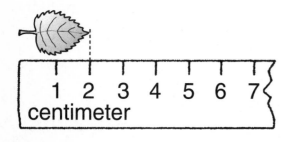

Ⓐ 2 centimeters, about 2 inches

Ⓑ 2 centimeters, almost 1 inch

Ⓒ 1 centimeter, about 2 inches

Ⓓ 1 centimeter, almost 1 inch

32. The bead is about 2 centimeters long. About how long is the whole string?

Ⓕ about 8 cm

Ⓖ about 6 cm

Ⓗ about 4 cm

Ⓙ about 2 cm

33. Use the ruler below to measure the pencil and the paper clip. How much longer is the pencil than the paper clip?

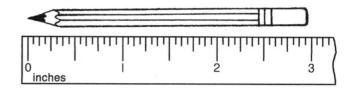

Ⓐ 1 in.

Ⓑ 2 in.

Ⓒ 3 in.

Ⓓ 4 in.

Name _____ Date _____

34. Min has a fence that is 18 feet long. She removes 4 feet of the fence to make a gate. Use the number line. How many feet of fence does Min have now?

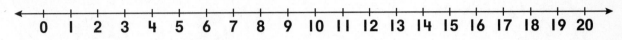

Ⓕ 4 feet   Ⓖ 14 feet   Ⓗ 15 feet   Ⓙ 18 feet

35. Ethan buys 32 yards of fabric. He recovers a sofa and has 15 yards of fabric left. Which equation can he use to find out how many yards of fabric he used for the sofa?

Ⓐ $32 - \square = 15$ yards

Ⓑ $32 - \square = 32$ yards

Ⓒ $32 + 15 = \square$ yards

Ⓓ $15 - \square = 32$ yards

36. Andrea makes a hair clip that is 8 centimeters long. She marks its length on a number line. She makes another hair clip that is 9 centimeters long. If she adds the length of the second hair clip, where will she mark the total on the number line?

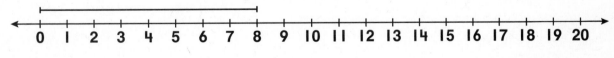

Ⓕ 15   Ⓖ 16   Ⓗ 18   Ⓙ Not Here

Pretest
Higher Scores on Math, Grade 2

Name _____   Date _____

37. Which time is shown on the clock?

Ⓐ 5:55

Ⓑ 6:55

Ⓒ 11:20

Ⓓ 11:30

38. The time is shown on the clock. If it is in the morning, what time is it?

Ⓕ 9:55 A.M.

Ⓖ 9:55 P.M.

Ⓗ 10:45 A.M.

Ⓙ 10:45 P.M.

39. Austin has the coins that are in the picture. What is the total value of the coins?

Ⓐ 30¢

Ⓑ 50¢

Ⓒ 55¢

Ⓓ 60¢

40. Brian has 1 dollar bill and 3 nickels. How much money does Brian have?

Ⓕ $1.15

Ⓖ $1.30

Ⓗ 110¢

Ⓙ 175¢

41. Latoya measures the lengths of some books. Use her list to complete the line plot. How many **✗**s should be above the 9?

Lengths of Books
6 inches
8 inches
9 inches
7 inches
8 inches

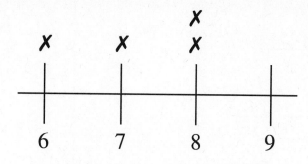

Lengths of Books in Inches

(A) 1   (B) 2   (C) 5   (D) 9

---

42. Look at the bar graph. How many balloons are NOT white?

COLORS OF BALLOONS

Color		Number of Balloons
White		
Gray		
Black		

0 1 2 3 4 5
Number of Balloons

(F) 2

(G) 3

(H) 4

(J) 5

43. Which shape has 5 sides?

Ⓐ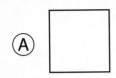

Ⓑ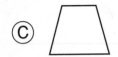

Ⓒ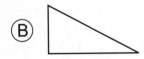

Ⓓ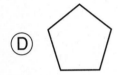

44. Which is one way to name this shape?

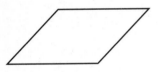

Ⓕ pentagon

Ⓖ quadrilateral

Ⓗ rectangle

Ⓙ triangle

45. How many equal faces are there on this figure?

Ⓐ 4

Ⓑ 3

Ⓒ 2

Ⓓ 0

46. Compare the square tile and the rectangle. How many tiles will cover the rectangle?

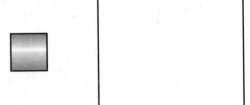

Ⓕ 4

Ⓖ 8

Ⓗ 9

Ⓙ 12

47. The dot paper represents centimeter squares. How many centimeter squares will fit inside the rectangle?

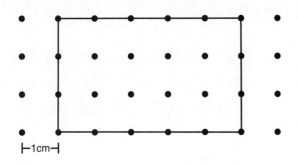

⊢1cm⊣

(A) 18

(B) 15

(C) 12

(D) 10

48. Which shape does NOT show equal shares?

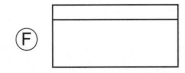
(F)

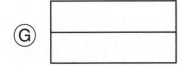
(G)

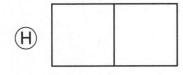
(H)

(J)

49. What part of the circle is shaded?

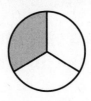

(A) a fourth of the shape

(B) a half of the shape

(C) a third of the shape

(D) Not Here

50. The square is divided into equal parts. Which is one way to describe the whole square that is shown?

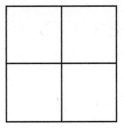

(F) two halves

(G) three thirds

(H) four fourths

(J) Not Here

Operations and Algebraic Thinking

Modeled Instruction

DIRECTIONS: Read each question and choose the best answer. Fill in the circle for the answer you have chosen.

1. Sal collects 45 cans for recycling. Amanda collects 39 cans for recycling. Which number sentence shows how to find the number of cans they collect altogether?

(A) $39 + \square = 45$

(B) $45 - 39 = \square$

(C) $45 + 39 = \square$

(D) $45 - \square = 39$

 Hint

The number of cans altogether is the sum of 45 and 39. Add to find the sum.

2. Maria has 5 ride tickets. She needs 7 ride tickets to ride the roller coaster. Adam gives her the extra tickets that she needs. How many tickets does Adam give Maria?

(F) 2

(G) 5

(H) 9

(J) 12

 Hint

Find the difference between the cost of the ride and the number of tickets that Maria already has. Use subtraction to find the difference.

Name _____   Date _____

3. At the school store, crayons cost 8 cents, a ruler costs 7 cents, and scissors cost 5 cents. Wanda has a jar of pennies to pay for these items. How many pennies does she need in all?

Ⓐ 12

Ⓑ 13

Ⓒ 15

Ⓓ 20

 Hint

Find the total by adding the cost of all three items. One penny equals one cent, so the number of cents in all is the same as the number of pennies in all.

4. Donnie and Luiz share a pizza. They each eat the same number of slices. The pizza has 6 slices. How many slices will each boy get?

Ⓕ 2

Ⓖ 3

Ⓗ 4

Ⓙ 6

 Hint

Use a drawing to show a pizza that has 6 equal parts. Then count the number of pieces in each half.

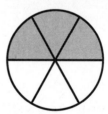

5. Justin has 14 marbles. He makes a group of 5 marbles and another group of marbles. Then he writes number sentences about the marbles. Which number will make both of these number sentences true?

$$\square + 5 = 14$$
$$14 - \square = 5$$

Ⓐ 9

Ⓑ 8

Ⓒ 7

Ⓓ 6

 Hint

Use mental math to think of what number added to 5 equals 14. Then try that number in the second sentence.

6. Sara has 3 white shirts, 2 light green shirts, and 4 dark green shirts. How many more green shirts does she have than white shirts?

Ⓕ 9

Ⓖ 6

Ⓗ 3

Ⓙ 1

 Hint

This is a two-step problem. First add light green shirts and dark green shirts to find the number of green shirts in all. Then subtract to compare the total number of green shirts to white shirts.

7. If you have 3 blue pens, 2 red pens, and 1 black pen, how many pens do you have in all?

Ⓐ 4

Ⓑ 5

Ⓒ 6

Ⓓ 7

 Hint

You can use two steps to add three numbers. Add two of the numbers. Then add the other number. You can also draw a picture to show the pens and then count the number in all.

8. If you take 6 marbles from this bag, how many will be left?

Ⓕ 5

Ⓖ 4

Ⓗ 3

Ⓙ 2

 Hint

Count to find that there are 8 marbles in the bag. Then use subtraction to take away 6 of the marbles.

9. Mr. Smith sells cars and trucks. He has 44 cars and 28 trucks. How many cars and trucks does he have altogether?

Ⓐ 84

Ⓑ 72

Ⓒ 62

Ⓓ 24

 Hint

Add to find the number altogether. Add the ones first and regroup 12 as 1 ten and 2 ones. Then add the tens. Be sure to include the regrouped ten.

10. Liz buys 20 oranges and 10 pineapples. How many more oranges than pineapples does she buy?

Ⓕ 5

Ⓖ 10

Ⓗ 20

Ⓙ 30

 Hint

Use subtraction to compare numbers of objects. Subtract the number of pineapples from the number of oranges.

11. Which number makes both of these sentences true?

$$6 + \square = 13$$
$$13 - 6 = \square$$

(A) 5

(B) 7

(C) 8

(D) 9

 Hint

Use a mental math doubles strategy to find the missing number. If you know that $6 + 6 = 12$, you can find the number added to 6 that makes 13. Then use the number in the second math sentence to check.

12. What is the missing number?

$$\square + 6 = 17$$

(F) 7

(G) 8

(H) 9

(J) 11

 Hint

Use a mental math tens strategy to find the missing number. If you know that $10 + 6 = 16$, you can find the number added to 6 that makes one more, 17.

13. Which number sentence does NOT equal 11?

   Ⓐ $7 + 3 = \square$

   Ⓑ $9 + 2 = \square$

   Ⓒ $12 - 1 = \square$

   Ⓓ $14 - 3 = \square$

 **Hint**

Use mental math to add or subtract each number sentence. Three of the answer choices will equal 11. Choose the one that does NOT equal 11.

14. Find the difference.

$$\begin{array}{r} 11 \\ -\ 4 \\ \hline \end{array}$$

   Ⓕ 15

   Ⓖ 13

   Ⓗ 7

   Ⓙ Not Here

 Hint

Use an addition fact to subtract. Think: What number plus 4 equals 11?

Name _____ Date _____

15. Find the sum.

$$5 + 3 + 5 = \square$$

Ⓐ 8

Ⓑ 10

Ⓒ 12

Ⓓ Not Here

 Hint

Group two of the numbers to make 10. Then add the other number.

16. Find the sum.

$$8 + 1 + 7 = \square$$

Ⓕ 16

Ⓖ 15

Ⓗ 14

Ⓙ Not Here

 Hint

Add the numbers in any order. If you add the 1 and 7 first, then you can use a doubles strategy to add.

Name _____ Date _____

17. Which pair of cube trains shows an even number?

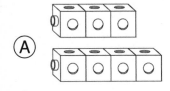

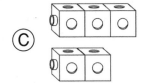

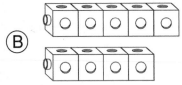

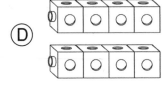

 Hint

An even number of cubes will make two rows that have the same number. Find the pair of cube trains that are the same length.

---

18. Which row of apples shows an odd number?

Ⓕ 🍎🍎🍎🍎🍎🍎🍎🍎🍎🍎

Ⓖ 🍎🍎🍎🍎🍎🍎🍎🍎🍎🍎🍎

Ⓗ 🍎🍎🍎🍎🍎🍎🍎

Ⓙ 🍎🍎🍎🍎🍎🍎🍎🍎🍎

 Hint

Make as many pairs as you can in each row of apples. The row with 1 apple left over shows an odd number.

Operations and Algebraic Thinking
Higher Scores on Math, Grade 2

19. Which number sentence correctly describes this group of ladybugs as an even number?

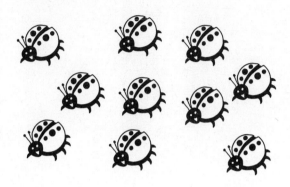

Ⓐ 10 = 5 + 5

Ⓑ 11 = 5 + 6

Ⓒ 12 = 6 + 6

Ⓓ 13 = 6 + 7

 Hint

An even number of ladybugs will make two equal groups. Choose the number sentence that shows the total number of ladybugs as a double.

20. Which number sentence correctly describes this group of flies as an odd number?

Ⓕ 6 = 2 + 2 + 2

Ⓖ 8 = 4 + 4

Ⓗ 9 = 4 + 4 + 1

Ⓙ 11 = 5 + 5 + 1

 Hint

An odd number of flies will not make two equal groups. There will be 1 fly left over. Choose the number sentence that shows the total number of flies as a double plus 1.

21. Count the stars. What is the next even number?

Ⓐ 9

Ⓑ 15

Ⓒ 16

Ⓓ 18

⭐ **Hint**

Decide whether the number of stars is even or odd. If it is odd, add 1 to make the number even. If it is even, add 2 to find the next even number.

22. Which number sentence can you use to find the total number of drums?

Ⓕ 4 + 4 + 4 + 4 = ☐

Ⓖ 5 + 5 + 5 + 5 = ☐

Ⓗ 5 + 5 + 5 + 5 + 5 = ☐

Ⓙ 10 + 5 = ☐

⭐ **Hint**

Add equal groups to find the number in all. There are 4 rows of 5 drums in the picture. The addition sentence should have 4 addends. Each addend is the number in each row.

23. Which number sentence shows how many squares are in this picture?

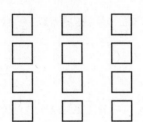

Ⓐ 3 + 4 = 7

Ⓑ 3 + 3 + 3 = 9

Ⓒ 4 + 4 = 8

Ⓓ 4 + 4 + 4 = 12

 Hint

Add equal groups to find the number in all. There are 4 rows of 3 squares each. You can add 3 four times or add 4 three times to find the total.

24. Sasha places her rock collection in a box. She makes 2 rows of 5 rocks. How many rocks does Sasha have in the box?

Ⓕ 15

Ⓖ 10

Ⓗ 7

Ⓙ 3

 Hint

Use objects or draw a picture to show a row of 5 rocks. Make another row of 5 rocks. Then add.

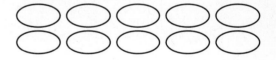

Operations and Algebraic Thinking
Higher Scores on Math, Grade 2

Operations and Algebraic Thinking

Independent Practice

DIRECTIONS: Read each question and choose the best answer. Fill in the circle for the answer you have chosen. If the correct answer is not available, mark the letter for "Not Here."

25. There are 24 students in Mr. Stone's class. Six students bring lunches from home. Which number sentence shows how to find the number of students who do NOT bring lunch from home?

Ⓐ $24 - 6 = \square$

Ⓑ $\square - 6 = 24$

Ⓒ $24 + 6 = \square$

Ⓓ $\square \times 6 = 24$

26. Ms. Sánchez has 30 baseball caps. She gives away 12 caps. How many caps does she have left?

Ⓕ 12

Ⓖ 18

Ⓗ 22

Ⓙ 42

27. Jack is 13. Manuel is 3 years younger than Jack. Janet is 5 years younger than Manuel. How old is Janet?

Ⓐ 16

Ⓑ 10

Ⓒ 8

Ⓓ 5

28. Andy eats 7 pretzels. Cassie eats 5 pretzels. How many pretzels do Andy and Cassie eat altogether?

Ⓕ 2

Ⓖ 4

Ⓗ 11

Ⓙ 12

29. Jessica has 17 ribbons. She makes a group of 8 ribbons and another group of ribbons. Then she writes number sentences about the ribbons. Which number will make both of these number sentences true?

$$\square + 8 = 17$$
$$17 - \square = 8$$

(A) 7

(B) 9

(C) 10

(D) 11

30. Tish has 14 toy turtles. She gives 8 turtles to her friends. How many turtles does Tish have left?

(F) 22

(G) 8

(H) 6

(J) 4

31. Ed sells 20 tops at the toy store one morning. Then he sells 16 more tops in the afternoon. How many tops does Ed sell altogether?

(A) 16

(B) 26

(C) 36

(D) 46

32. If you take 6 grapes from this group, how many will be left?

(F) 11

(G) 9

(H) 7

(J) 6

Name _____ Date _____

33. Josh has 82 dimes. He spends 24 dimes. How many dimes does he have left?

(A) 106

(B) 68

(C) 62

(D) 58

34. The teacher orders 15 calculators. Then she orders 7 more calculators. How many calculators does she order in all?

(F) 8

(G) 17

(H) 22

(J) 25

35. If there are 3 girls, 2 boys, and 1 adult on a bus, how many people are on the bus?

(A) 5

(B) 6

(C) 7

(D) 8

36. Meg counts blue jeans at school. She counts 17 jeans in one class. Then she counts 16 more jeans. How many jeans does she count in all?

(F) 33

(G) 23

(H) 11

(J) 1

37. Sam sees 29 giraffes at the zoo. There are 12 giraffes eating leaves. How many giraffes are NOT eating leaves?

(A) 41

(B) 31

(C) 17

(D) 7

38. Mrs. Garza has 47 cows on her ranch. She sells 23 cows. How many cows does she have left?

Ⓕ 13

Ⓖ 24

Ⓗ 37

Ⓙ 70

39. Mrs. Ramírez has 23 dolls in her collection. She gets 4 more dolls for her birthday. Which number sentence shows how many dolls she has in all?

Ⓐ $23 + 4 = \square$

Ⓑ $23 - 4 = \square$

Ⓒ $\square + 4 = 23$

Ⓓ $23 \times 4 = \square$

40. Dean has 33 bells. His aunt gives him 9 more bells. How many bells does Dean have altogether?

Ⓕ 13

Ⓖ 24

Ⓗ 34

Ⓙ 42

41. Karen picks 12 pink roses and 14 red roses. Then she gives away 5 roses. How many roses does Karen have left?

Ⓐ 19

Ⓑ 21

Ⓒ 26

Ⓓ 31

42. Jane picks 47 peaches in the morning and 35 peaches in the afternoon. Which sentence shows how many more peaches she picks in the morning than in the afternoon?

(F) $47 + 35 = \square$

(G) $\square + 47 = 35$

(H) $35 - \square = 45$

(J) $47 - 35 = \square$

43. There are 64 second-graders at Harris School. A total of 45 of them ride a bus to school. How many second-graders get to school another way?

(A) 19

(B) 20

(C) 21

(D) 29

44. Mark goes on a 95-mile bicycle trip. He rides 31 miles the first day and 36 miles the next day. How many more miles does he have to go?

(F) 28

(G) 59

(H) 64

(J) 67

45. There were 12 men, 17 women, and 17 children at a family reunion. How many people were there in all?

(A) 29

(B) 34

(C) 36

(D) 46

Operations and Algebraic Thinking
Higher Scores on Math, Grade 2

46. Carla has 72 stamps in her collection. She buys 3 more stamps. Then Aunt Martha gives her 4 stamps. Which number sentence shows how many stamps she has in all?

(F) $72 + 3 - 4 = \square$

(G) $72 - 3 + 4 = \square$

(H) $72 + 7 = \square$

(J) $72 - 7 = \square$

47. Which number makes both of these sentences true?

$$8 + \square = 14$$
$$14 - \square = 8$$

(A) 2

(B) 4

(C) 6

(D) 8

48. Which number makes both of these sentences true?

$$15 - \square = 6$$
$$6 + \square = 15$$

(F) 10

(G) 9

(H) 7

(J) 6

49. What is the missing number?

$$\square + 4 = 9$$

(A) 3

(B) 4

(C) 5

(D) 6

50. What is the missing number?

$$\boxed{\square - 6 = 7}$$

(F) 14

(G) 13

(H) 11

(J) 9

51. Which number sentence does NOT equal 17?

(A) $9 + 8 = \square$

(B) $10 + 7 = \square$

(C) $17 - 0 = \square$

(D) $20 - 4 = \square$

52. Which number sentence does NOT equal 14?

(F) $7 + 7 = \square$

(G) $8 + 6 = \square$

(H) $9 + 3 = \square$

(J) $10 + 4 = \square$

53. Find the sum.

$$\begin{array}{r} 2 \\ + 9 \\ \hline \end{array}$$

(A) 11

(B) 10

(C) 7

(D) Not Here

54. Find the difference.

$$\begin{array}{r} 18 \\ - 9 \\ \hline \end{array}$$

(F) 7

(G) 8

(H) 11

(J) Not Here

55. Find the sum.

$$6 + 1 + 4 = \square$$

(A) 7

(B) 11

(C) 12

(D) Not Here

56. What is the missing number?

$$8 + 2 + 5 = \square$$

(F) 15

(G) 13

(H) 10

(J) Not Here

57. Find the sum.

$$7 + 6 + 3 = \square$$

(A) 17

(B) 13

(C) 9

(D) Not Here

58. What is the missing number?

$$9 + 5 + 5 = \square$$

(F) 10

(G) 14

(H) 19

(J) Not Here

59. Find the difference.

$$13 - 10 = \square$$

(A) 7

(B) 4

(C) 3

(D) Not Here

60. Find the sum.

$$7 + 7 = \square$$

(F) 12

(G) 13

(H) 16

(J) Not Here

61. Which pair of cube trains shows an odd number?

(A)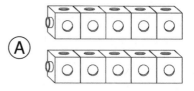

(B)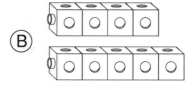

(C)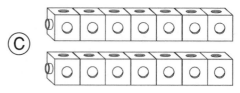

(D)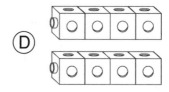

62. Which number sentence correctly describes this group of baseballs as an even number?

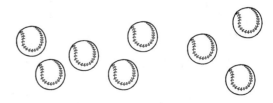

(F) $6 = 3 + 3$

(G) $8 = 4 + 4$

(H) $9 = 4 + 5$

(J) $10 = 6 + 4$

63. Which row of baseball gloves shows an even number?

Ⓐ

Ⓑ

Ⓒ

Ⓓ

---

64. Which number sentence correctly describes this group of footballs as an odd number?

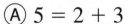

Ⓕ $10 = 5 + 5$ Ⓗ $12 = 6 + 6$

Ⓖ $11 = 5 + 5 + 1$ Ⓙ $13 = 6 + 6 + 1$

---

65. Which number sentence correctly describes this group of basketballs as an even number?

Ⓐ $5 = 2 + 3$ Ⓒ $7 = 3 + 4$

Ⓑ $6 = 3 + 3$ Ⓓ $8 = 4 + 4$

Name _____ Date _____

66. Count the cowboy hats. What is the next odd number?

(F) 7

(G) 8

(H) 9

(J) 10

67. Count the party hats. What is the next even number?

(A) 12

(B) 13

(C) 14

(D) 15

68. Which number sentence has a sum that is an even number?

(F) $9 + 9 = \square$

(G) $8 + 7 = \square$

(H) $7 + 6 = \square$

(J) $6 + 5 = \square$

69. Which number sentence has a sum that is an odd number?

(A) $3 + 3 = \square$

(B) $6 + 6 = \square$

(C) $7 + 7 = \square$

(D) $8 + 9 = \square$

70. Jana has 16 marbles, and Dee has 9 marbles. Andrew has 15 marbles, and Cody has 10 marbles. Which two people each have an even number of marbles?

(F) Andrew and Jana

(G) Cody and Dee

(H) Dee and Andrew

(J) Jana and Cody

71. Mason puts his toy cars in 3 rows. There are 4 cars in each row. Which addition sentence correctly describes the number of cars?

(A) $3 + 4 = 7$

(B) $3 + 3 + 3 = 9$

(C) $4 + 4 + 4 = 12$

(D) $4 + 4 + 4 + 4 = 16$

72. Look at the stars. Which addition sentence can you use to find the total number of stars?

(F) $4 + 4 + 4 + 4 = \square$

(G) $5 + 5 + 5 + 5 + 5 = \square$

(H) $6 + 6 + 6 + 6 = \square$

(J) $10 + 10 = \square$

73. Tia has a new photo album. Each page will fit 4 rows of 2 pictures each. How many pictures will fit on each page?

(A) 4

(B) 6

(C) 7

(D) 8

74. Clark puts his baseball cards in 3 rows. There are 3 cards in each row. Which number sentence shows how many baseball cards Clark has?

(F) $3 + 0 = 3$

(G) $3 + 3 = 6$

(H) $3 + 3 + 3 = 9$

(J) $3 + 3 + 3 + 3 = 12$

75. Which number sentence matches the number of baskets in this picture?

- Ⓐ $2 + 2 = 4$
- Ⓑ $2 + 2 + 2 = 6$
- Ⓒ $4 + 4 = 8$
- Ⓓ $4 + 4 + 4 = 12$

76. The array shows 2 rows of 5 squares. Which number sentence shows one way to add the circles?

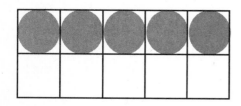

- Ⓕ $1 + 5 = 6$
- Ⓖ $2 + 5 = 7$
- Ⓗ $5 + 5 = 10$
- Ⓙ $5 + 0 = 5$

77. The array shows 5 rows of 5 squares. Which number sentence shows one way to add the circles?

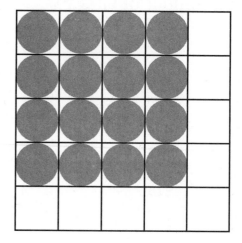

- Ⓐ $4 + 4 + 4 = 12$
- Ⓑ $4 + 4 + 4 + 4 = 16$
- Ⓒ $5 + 5 + 5 + 5 = 20$
- Ⓓ $5 + 5 + 5 + 5 + 5 = 25$

78. Which number sentence shows how many ink blots are in this picture?

- Ⓕ $5 + 5 + 5 = 15$
- Ⓖ $5 + 5 = 10$
- Ⓗ $3 + 3 + 3 = 9$
- Ⓙ $3 + 5 = 8$

Operations and Algebraic Thinking
Higher Scores on Math, Grade 2

Number and Operations in Base Ten

Modeled Instruction

DIRECTIONS: Read each question and choose the best answer. Fill in the circle for the answer you have chosen.

1. The model shows a number of hundreds, tens, and ones. What is the number?

Hundreds	Tens	Ones

(A) 247

(B) 274

(C) 427

(D) 724

 Hint

The order of the digits in a 3-digit number is hundreds, tens, and then ones. The model shows 4 hundreds flats, 2 tens rods, and 7 ones cubes.

2. How many hundreds, tens, and ones are in 803?

(F) 80 hundreds, 0 tens, 3 ones

(G) 8 hundreds, 0 tens, 3 ones

(H) 3 tens, 0 hundreds, 8 ones

(J) 3 hundreds, 0 tens, 8 ones

Hint

The 8 is in the hundreds place, the 0 is in the tens place, and the 3 is in the ones place. There is only one digit in each place.

3. The model shows groups of 10 tens. Which statement does the model prove?

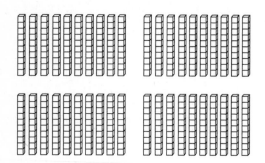

(A) 4 tens = 400

(B) 4 tens = 40 hundreds

(C) 40 tens = 40

(D) 40 tens = 4 hundreds

 Hint

Count the tens. Count the groups of 10 tens. One group of 10 tens equals 1 hundred.

4. Look at the place-value model. What value does it show?

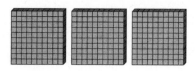

(F) 300

(G) 30

(H) 3 tens

(J) 3 ones

 Hint

The place-value model shows hundreds. Count the number of hundreds shown.

5. Count by fives. What number comes next?

| 165, 170, 175, 180, □ |

Ⓐ 180

Ⓑ 185

Ⓒ 190

Ⓓ 195

 Hint

When you count by fives, the digit in the ones place changes 5, 0, 5, 0, 5, 0, and so on. Think of the next number greater than 180 that has 5 in the ones place.

6. Count by tens. What number comes next?

| 380, 390, 400, □ |

Ⓕ 401

Ⓖ 405

Ⓗ 410

Ⓙ 500

 Hint

When you count by tens, the digit in the ones place is always 0. Think of the next number greater than 400 that ends with 0 and is only 10 more than 400.

7. Which does NOT name the number shown by the model?

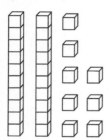

Ⓐ two hundred eight

Ⓑ twenty-eight

Ⓒ 2 tens 8 ones

Ⓓ 28

 Hint

The model has no hundreds. You can count the number of tens and ones. You can also count the total number of cubes.

8. Which number is eighty-nine?

Ⓕ 908

Ⓖ 809

Ⓗ 98

Ⓙ 89

 Hint

Think of eighty-nine as 80 plus 9 more. Choose the number that has 8 in the tens place and 9 in the ones place.

9. Compare the numbers. Which symbol belongs in the box?

$$457 \ \square \ 475$$

(A) $<$

(B) $=$

(C) $>$

(D) Not Here

 Hint

Compare hundreds. They are the same. Then compare tens. Five tens are less than 7 tens, so the first number is less than the second number. The symbol for *less than* is $<$.

10. Compare the models. Which comparison do they show?

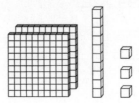

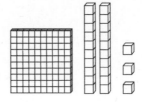

(F) $213 < 123$

(G) $213 = 123$

(H) $213 > 123$

(J) $213 > 132$

 Hint

The models show 213 and 123. Two hundreds are greater than one hundred, so you do not need to compare the tens and ones. The symbol for *greater than* is $>$.

11. Which number completes the number sentence?

$$70 + 20 = \square$$

Ⓐ 9

Ⓑ 50

Ⓒ 90

Ⓓ 100

 Hint

Both addends have 0 ones. Use mental math to add 7 tens plus 2 tens.

12. The model shows two ways to make 50. What is $50 - 26$?

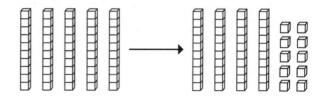

Ⓕ 14

Ⓖ 24

Ⓗ 36

Ⓙ 76

 Hint

The model shows that 5 tens is the same as 4 tens and 10 ones. Use the model to subtract 2 tens and 6 ones from 4 tens and 10 ones.

13. Clint uses a calculator to add $26 + 46 = 72$. Which number sentence below can he also answer from this calculation?

(A) $72 + 46 = \square$

(B) $72 - 46 = \square$

(C) $46 - 26 = \square$

(D) $26 + 72 = \square$

 Hint

You can change the order of the addends to find the same sum. You can also subtract either addend from the sum to find the other addend.

14. Find the sum.

$$35 + 31 + 15 = \square$$

(F) 46

(G) 50

(H) 66

(J) 81

 Hint

Add the numbers in any order. Add 35 and 15 first to make 50, and then add 31.

15. Find the sum.

$$\begin{array}{r} \square \\ 21 \\ 25 \\ 14 \\ +\ 32 \\ \hline \end{array}$$

(A) 12   (B) 72   (C) 82   (D) 92

 Hint

Add the ones first: $1 + 5 + 4 + 2 = 12$. Regroup the ones as 1 ten and 2 ones. Then add the tens: $1 + 2 + 2 + 1 + 3 = 9$.

---

16. Use models to add $421 + 264$. What is the sum?

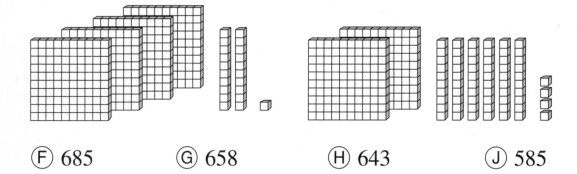

(F) 685   (G) 658   (H) 643   (J) 585

 Hint

Count the total number of hundreds, tens, and ones. Use the results to find the 3-digit number.

17. Use a place-value chart to add 334 + 275. Regroup if you need to. What is the sum?

Hundreds	Tens	Ones
☐		
3	3	4
+ 2	7	5

Ⓐ 509

Ⓑ 519

Ⓒ 609

Ⓓ 691

 Hint

Add the ones first. There is no need to regroup the ones. Then add the tens. Regroup 10 tens as 1 hundred and 0 tens. Then add the hundreds. Be sure to include the regrouped hundred.

18. Use mental math to add 279 + 10. What is the sum?

Ⓕ 179

Ⓖ 269

Ⓗ 280

Ⓙ 289

 Hint

To add 10 to any number, increase the number of tens by 1. All other digits in the number stay the same.

19. Use mental math to subtract 942 − 100. What is the difference?

Ⓐ 742

Ⓑ 842

Ⓒ 932

Ⓓ 941

 Hint

To subtract 100 from any number, decrease the number of hundreds by 1. All other digits in the number stay the same.

20. Caitlyn uses place-value blocks to subtract 43 − 17. Why does she rename 43 as 3 tens and 13 ones?

Ⓕ She cannot subtract 3 ones − 7 ones.

Ⓖ She cannot subtract 4 tens − 1 ten.

Ⓗ She cannot subtract 7 ones − 3 ones.

Ⓙ She cannot subtract 1 ten − 4 tens.

 Hint

Subtract the ones first. If there are not enough ones in the first number, you must regroup the tens as 1 less ten and 10 ones. Caitlyn renames 43 to get 3 tens and 13 ones. Then she subtracts 13 ones − 7 ones.

Number and Operations in Base Ten

Independent Practice

DIRECTIONS: Read each question and choose the best answer. Fill in the circle for the answer you have chosen. If the correct answer is not available, mark the letter for "Not Here."

21. The model shows a number of hundreds, tens, and ones. What is the number?

Hundreds	Tens	Ones

Ⓐ 123

Ⓑ 213

Ⓒ 312

Ⓓ 321

22. How many hundreds, tens, and ones are in 540?

Ⓕ 0 hundreds, 4 tens, 5 ones

Ⓖ 4 hundreds, 5 tens, 0 ones

Ⓗ 5 hundreds, 0 tens, 4 ones

Ⓙ 5 hundreds, 4 tens, 0 ones

23. Which number has a 3 in the tens place?

Ⓐ 134

Ⓑ 143

Ⓒ 341

Ⓓ 413

24. Look at the place-value model. What is the number that it shows?

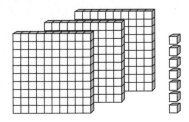

F 370

G 317

H 307

J 37

25. The model shows groups of 10 tens. Which statement does the model prove?

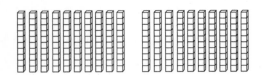

A 2 tens = 2 hundreds

B 2 tens = 20 hundreds

C 20 tens = 20

D 20 tens = 200

26. Marcie uses 70 tens rods to show a number. She draws a circle around each group of 10 tens. What number does Marcie show?

F 7,000

G 700

H 70

J 7

27. Which value is the same as 900?

A 9 ones, 0 tens, 0 hundreds

B 9 tens, 0 hundreds, 0 ones

C 9 hundreds, 0 tens, 0 ones

D 9 hundreds, 9 tens, 9 ones

28. Look at the place-value model. What value does it show?

Ⓕ 400

Ⓖ 300

Ⓗ 40

Ⓙ 30

29. Count by fives. What number comes next?

| 210, 215, 220, 225, □ |

Ⓐ 226

Ⓑ 230

Ⓒ 235

Ⓓ 240

30. Count by tens. What number comes next?

| 570, 580, 590, □ |

Ⓕ 500

Ⓖ 591

Ⓗ 595

Ⓙ 600

31. Which number belongs in the box?

| 500, 600, 700, □, 900 |

Ⓐ 800

Ⓑ 750

Ⓒ 710

Ⓓ 1,000

32. Which number belongs in the box?

310, 315, 320, □, 330

Ⓕ 321 Ⓗ 335

Ⓖ 325 Ⓙ 340

33. Which number is one hundred thirteen?

Ⓐ 131 Ⓒ 113

Ⓑ 130 Ⓓ 103

34. How should you read 306?

Ⓕ three hundred six

Ⓖ three hundred sixty

Ⓗ thirty-six

Ⓙ three hundred sixteen

35. Which value is the same as five hundred forty-seven?

Ⓐ 50 + 47

Ⓑ 5 + 4 + 7

Ⓒ 574

Ⓓ 500 + 40 + 7

36. Which does NOT name the number shown by the model?

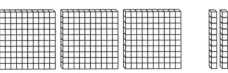

Ⓕ 325

Ⓖ three hundred twenty-five

Ⓗ 5 hundreds, 2 tens, 5 ones

Ⓙ 300 + 20 + 5

37. Compare the models. Which comparison do they show?

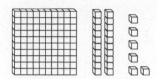

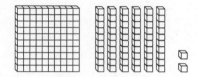

(A) $126 > 162$

(B) $126 = 162$

(C) $126 < 162$

(D) Not Here

38. Compare the models. Which comparison do they show?

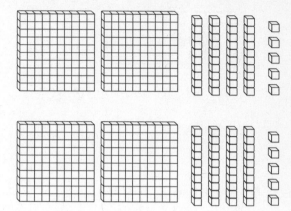

(F) $145 > 245$

(G) $245 = 245$

(H) $245 < 254$

(J) Not Here

39. Compare the numbers. Which symbol belongs in the box?

$$865 \ \square \ 756$$

(A) >   (C) <

(B) =   (D) +

40. Compare the numbers. Which symbol belongs in the box?

$$599 \ \square \ 601$$

(F) >   (H) <

(G) =   (J) +

41. Which number completes the number sentence?

$$80 - 40 = \square$$

(A) 4   (C) 70

(B) 40   (D) 120

42. Which number completes the number sentence?

$$56 + 14 = \square$$

(F) 42   (H) 60

(G) 52   (J) 70

43. The models show 27 and 18. What is 27 + 18?

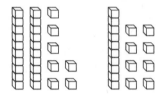

(A) 32   (C) 42

(B) 35   (D) 45

44. The model shows one way to make 32. What is 32 − 13?

(F) 19 (H) 15

(G) 17 (J) 11

45. Tanisha uses a calculator to subtract 91 − 49 = 42. Which number sentence below can she also answer from this calculation?

(A) 42 + 49 = □

(B) 42 + 91 = □

(C) 49 + 91 = □

(D) 49 − 42 = □

46. Find the sum.

$$\begin{array}{r} \square \\ 15 \\ + \ 35 \\ \hline \end{array}$$

(F) 40 (H) 50

(G) 45 (J) Not Here

47. Find the difference.

$$\begin{array}{r} \square \\ 66 \\ - \ 28 \\ \hline \end{array}$$

(A) 28 (C) 42

(B) 38 (D) Not Here

48. What is the missing number?

10 + 53 + 30 = □

(F) 40 (H) 83

(G) 63 (J) 93

49. Find the sum.

26 + 24 + 11 = □

(A) 42 (C) 61

(B) 50 (D) 71

50. Find the sum.

$$\begin{array}{r} \square \\ 30 \\ 16 \\ 11 \\ +\ 27 \\ \hline \end{array}$$

Ⓕ 74   Ⓗ 94

Ⓖ 84   Ⓙ Not Here

51. Find the sum.

$$\begin{array}{r} \square \\ 14 \\ 15 \\ 16 \\ +\ 17 \\ \hline \end{array}$$

Ⓐ 48   Ⓒ 60

Ⓑ 52   Ⓓ Not Here

52. Use models to add 163 + 163. What is the sum?

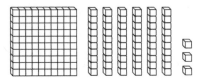

Ⓕ 326   Ⓗ 306

Ⓖ 316   Ⓙ 226

53. Use a model to subtract 427 − 104. What is the difference?

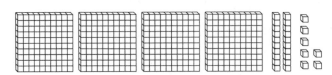

Ⓐ 223   Ⓒ 323

Ⓑ 303   Ⓓ 333

Number and Operations in Base Ten
Higher Scores on Math, Grade 2

54. Sanjaya uses a calculator to add $625 + 147 = 772$. Which number sentence below can he also answer from this calculation?

(F) $772 - 625 = \square$

(G) $772 + 625 = \square$

(H) $625 - 147 = \square$

(J) $147 + 772 = \square$

55. Dannah uses a calculator to subtract $358 - 209 = 149$. Which number sentence below can she also answer from this calculation?

(A) $358 + 149 = \square$

(B) $209 - 149 = \square$

(C) $209 + 358 = \square$

(D) $149 + 209 = \square$

56. Use a place-value chart to add $526 + 115$. Regroup if you need to. What is the sum?

Hundreds	Tens	Ones
$\square$	$\square$	
5	2	6
+ 1	1	5

(F) 741   (H) 631

(G) 641   (J) Not Here

57. Use a place-value chart to subtract $742 - 380$. Regroup if you need to. What is the difference?

Hundreds	Tens	Ones
$\square$	$\square$	
7	4	2
− 3	8	0

(A) 362   (C) 462

(B) 442   (D) 482

58. Use mental math to add
475 + 100. What is the sum?

(F) 375   (H) 675

(G) 485   (J) Not Here

59. Use mental math to subtract
604 − 10. What is the
difference?

(A) 614   (C) 506

(B) 594   (D) 504

60. Use mental math to add
712 + 10. What is the sum?

(F) 612   (H) 722

(G) 702   (J) 812

61. Nate wants to add
16 + 19 + 14. Why does first
adding 16 + 14 = 30 make
the addition easier?

(A) He does not need to add
19 more.

(B) It does not work. He
cannot change the order.

(C) He can use mental math to
add 30 + 19.

(D) He can estimate
20 + 20 + 14.

62. Julia uses place-value blocks
to subtract 358 − 171. Why
does she rename 358 as
2 hundreds, 15 tens, 8 ones?

(F) There are not enough
hundreds to subtract.

(G) There are not enough tens
to subtract.

(H) There are not enough ones
to subtract.

(J) Not Here

Name _____ Date _____

Measurement and Data

Modeled Instruction

DIRECTIONS: Read each question and choose the best answer. Fill in the circle for the answer you have chosen.

1. Use the inch ruler to measure. About how long is the crayon?

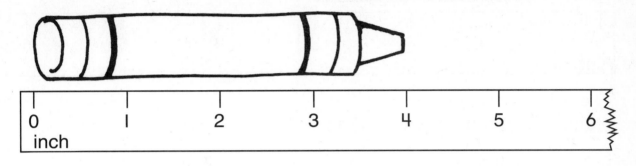

(A) 1 inch   (B) 2 inches   (C) 3 inches   (D) 4 inches

 Hint

Measure the length of the crayon from 0 on the ruler. Find the number on the ruler nearest where the crayon ends.

---

2. A lampshade has a round edge. Which is the best tool for measuring around the edge of a lampshade?

(F) centimeter ruler   (H) meter stick

(G) measuring tape   (J) yardstick

 Hint

Choose the tool that will measure objects that are not flat.

3. Measure the leaf in centimeters and in inches. About how long is the leaf?

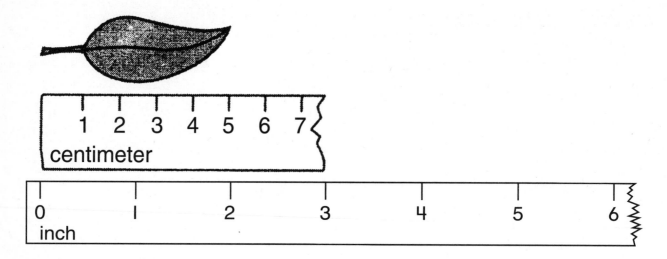

Ⓐ about 2 centimeters, about 5 inches

Ⓑ about 5 centimeters, about 2 inches

Ⓒ about 5 centimeters, about 5 inches

Ⓓ about 7 centimeters, about 3 inches

 Hint

Make sure to line up rulers to start with 0. If a ruler does not mark the 0, use the edge of the ruler. Note that the number of centimeters is greater than the number of inches.

4. Jenna cuts a string 2 inches long. Paulo cuts a string 2 feet long. Who cuts the longer piece of string? How do you know?

    (F) Jenna, because inches are longer than feet

    (G) Jenna, because feet are longer than inches

    (H) Paulo, because inches are longer than feet

    (J) Paulo, because feet are longer than inches

 **Hint**

There are 12 inches in one foot. A child's finger is about 2 inches long. A man's arm is about 2 feet long. Choose the name first. Then choose the reason why the name is correct.

5. The paper clip is about 1 inch long. About how long is the slice of fruit?

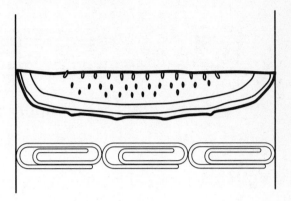

    (A) about 7 inches

    (B) about 5 inches

    (C) about 3 inches

    (D) about 1 inch

 Hint

Use the paper clip to estimate the length of 1 inch. Find about how many paper clips equal the length of the fruit.

6. Each cube is about 1 centimeter long. About how long is the ribbon?

Ⓕ about 8 cm   Ⓖ about 6 cm   Ⓗ about 4 cm   Ⓙ about 2 cm

 Hint

The ribbon is about the same length as 4 pairs of cubes. Count 2, 4, 6, 8.

---

7. Use the ruler below to measure the pencil and the eraser. How much longer is the pencil than the eraser?

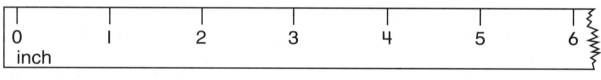

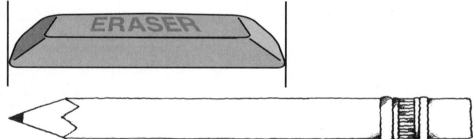

Ⓐ 2 in.   Ⓑ 3 in.   Ⓒ 4 in.   Ⓓ 5 in.

 Hint

Use the ruler to measure both items. Subtract the longer length from the shorter one to compare the lengths.

Name _____   Date _____

8. Henry replaces a part of his fence that is 17 feet long. He also replaces a part of the fence that is 15 feet. Use the number line. How many feet of fence does Henry replace in all?

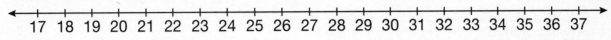

17 18 19 20 21 22 23 24 25 26 27 28 29 30 31 32 33 34 35 36 37

(F) 2 feet   (G) 22 feet   (H) 32 feet   (J) 34 feet

 Hint

Start at 17 and count forward 15 hops on the number line. The number where you land is the sum of 17 and 15.

---

9. Abby buys 54 yards of fabric. She makes some curtains and has 14 yards of fabric left. How many yards does she use for the curtains?

| 54 yards − ☐ yards = 14 yards |

(A) 30 yards   (B) 40 yards   (C) 48 yards   (D) 68 yards

 Hint

Use the equation to subtract the lengths and find the missing number of yards.

10. Lucas makes two flags that are each 8 feet long. He uses a number line to show the length of one flag. If he adds the length of the other flag, where will he land on the number line?

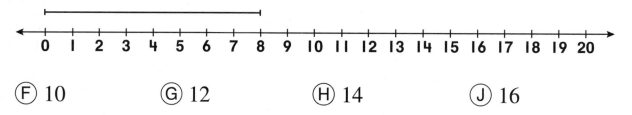

(F) 10   (G) 12   (H) 14   (J) 16

 Hint

Start from the end of the first length. Draw a line that is 8 more units long. The number where you end is the sum.

---

11. Brianna subtracts 75 inches − 30 inches on a number line. First she draws a line from 0 to 75 to show 75 inches. If she then draws a line to count back by 30, where will she land on the number line?

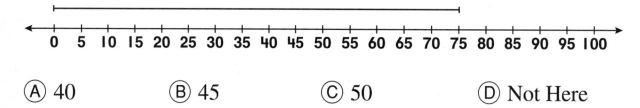

(A) 40   (B) 45   (C) 50   (D) Not Here

 Hint

Start from 75 and skip count backward by fives. Count 5, 10, 15, 20, 25, 30. The number where you land is the difference.

12. Which time is shown on the clock?

(F) 3:55

(G) 4:55

(H) 11:20

(J) 11:40

 Hint

Name the hour first. The hour hand is shorter than the minute hand. It points a little past 11, so the hour is 11. Then count by fives to find the minutes. Count 5, 10, 15, 20.

13. The time is early in the morning. Which time is shown on the clock?

(A) 6:25 P.M.

(B) 6:25 A.M.

(C) 5:30 P.M.

(D) 5:30 A.M.

 Hint

Name the hour first, then the minutes. A.M. times are between midnight and noon. P.M. times are between noon and midnight.

14. Sue has 2 quarters and 3 nickels. How much money does Sue have in all?

(F) 65¢

(G) 70¢

(H) 75¢

(J) 90¢

Hint

One quarter equals 25 cents. One nickel equals 5 cents. Use the coins that have the greatest value first. Count the quarters by 25s. Count 25, 50. Then count on by fives to add 3 nickels. From 50, count 55, 60, 65.

15. Martin has money in his pocket that matches the picture. How much money does Martin have in his pocket?

(A) $10.40

(B) 10.40¢

(C) $1.40

(D) $140¢

Hint

Find the number of dollars first. Then add the value of each coin to find the total number of cents. Be sure to choose a correct way to write a money amount.

16. Fatima measures the lengths of some pencils. Use her list to complete the line plot. How many **✗**s should be above the 7?

Lengths of Pencils
4 inches
7 inches
5 inches
7 inches
6 inches

```
 ✗        ✗        ✗
 |        |        |        |
─┼────────┼────────┼────────┼──
 |        |        |        |
 4        5        6        7
```

Lengths of Pencils in Inches

Ⓕ 1   Ⓖ 2   Ⓗ 5   Ⓙ 7

 Hint

The number of **✗**s above each number should be the same as the number of pencils matching that length. Count the number of pencils that are 7 inches long.

Name _____ Date _____

17. Use the ruler to measure the ropes. Which line plot matches the data?

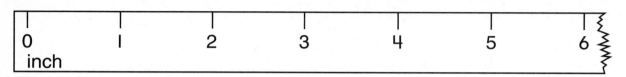

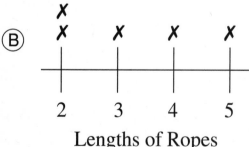

Ⓐ
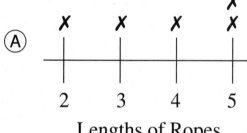

Lengths of Ropes
in Inches

Ⓒ
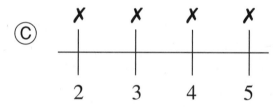

Lengths of Ropes
in Inches

Ⓑ

```
X
X       X    X    X
+---+----+----+----+
2   3    4    5
```

Lengths of Ropes
in Inches

Ⓓ

```
X
X              X    X
+---+----+----+----+
2   3    4    5
```

Lengths of Ropes
in Inches

⭐ **Hint**

The number of **X**s above each number should be the same as the number of ropes matching that length.

18. Miss Finch counts the balls that she puts outside for field day. The table shows 1 tally mark for each ball. Which picture graph matches the table?

Balls on the Field		
Footballs	🏈	IIII
Baseballs	⚾	⊬⊬⊬ IIII
Basketballs	🏀	⊬⊬⊬ I

(F)
Footballs	🏁 🏁 🏁 🏁 🏁 🏁 🏁 🏁 🏁 🏁
Baseballs	🏁 🏁 🏁 🏁 🏁 🏁 🏁 🏁 🏁 🏁
Basketballs	🏁 🏁 🏁 🏁 🏁 🏁 🏁 🏁 🏁 🏁

Key: Each 🏁 stands for 1.

(G)
Footballs	🏁 🏁 🏁 🏁 🏁 🏁 🏁 🏁
Baseballs	🏁 🏁 🏁 🏁
Basketballs	🏁 🏁 🏁 🏁 🏁 🏁

Key: Each 🏁 stands for 1.

(H)
Footballs	🏁 🏁 🏁 🏁
Baseballs	🏁 🏁 🏁 🏁 🏁 🏁 🏁 🏁
Basketballs	🏁 🏁 🏁 🏁 🏁 🏁

Key: Each 🏁 stands for 1.

(J)
Footballs	🏁 🏁 🏁 🏁 🏁 🏁
Baseballs	🏁 🏁 🏁 🏁 🏁 🏁 🏁 🏁 🏁
Basketballs	🏁 🏁 🏁 🏁

Key: Each 🏁 stands for 1.

 Hint

Count the number of whistles in each row. Make sure the number of whistles in each row matches the number of tally marks in the table.

19. Look at the bar graph. Which animal is there the most of in the barn?

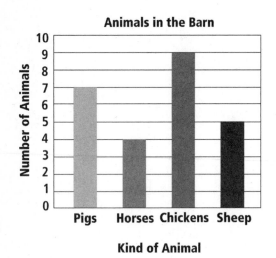

Animals in the Barn

Kind of Animal

Ⓐ chickens

Ⓑ horses

Ⓒ pigs

Ⓓ sheep

 Hint

Compare the lengths of the bars in the graph. The tallest bar shows the most animals.

20. Look at the bar graph. How many children in all named their favorite juice?

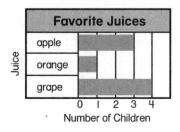

Favorite Juices

Ⓕ 12

Ⓖ 8

Ⓗ 4

Ⓙ 3

 Hint

Add all three numbers that the bars show.

Measurement and Data

Independent Practice

DIRECTIONS: Read each question and choose the best answer. Fill in the circle for the answer you have chosen. If the correct answer is not available, mark the letter for "Not Here."

21. Each paper clip is about 1 inch long. About how long is the crayon?

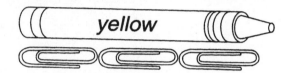

(A) 1 inch

(B) 2 inches

(C) 3 inches

(D) 4 inches

22. An apple seed is very small. Which is the best tool for measuring the length of an apple seed?

(F) centimeter ruler

(G) measuring tape

(H) meter stick

(J) yardstick

23. Which is the best tool for measuring the length of a hallway?

(A) centimeter ruler

(B) inch ruler

(C) paper clips

(D) yardstick

24. Use the centimeter ruler to measure. About how long is the feather?

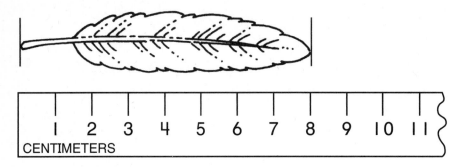

(F) 6 centimeters

(G) 8 centimeters

(H) 10 centimeters

(J) 12 centimeters

---

25. Use the inch ruler to measure. About how long is the toothbrush?

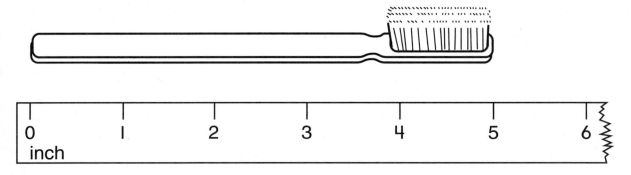

(A) 5 inches

(B) 4 inches

(C) 3 inches

(D) 2 inches

Name _____   Date _____

26. Measure the pencil in inches and in centimeters. About how long is the pencil?

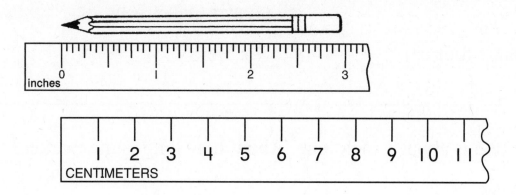

   (F) about 8 inches, about 3 centimeters

   (G) about 8 inches, about 8 centimeters

   (H) about 3 inches, about 3 centimeters

   (J) about 3 inches, about 8 centimeters

---

27. Gary cuts a board 4 meters long. Cici cuts a board 4 centimeters long. Who cuts the longer board? How do you know?

   (A) Gary, because centimeters are longer than meters

   (B) Gary, because meters are longer than centimeters

   (C) Cici, because centimeters are longer than meters

   (D) Cici, because meters are longer than centimeters

28. Vanya's new baseball bat is about 1 yard long. If he measures the baseball bat in feet, what is the length?

    Ⓕ 1 foot   Ⓗ greater than 1 foot

    Ⓖ less than 1 foot   Ⓙ Not Here

29. The paper clip is about 1 inch long. About how long is the marker?

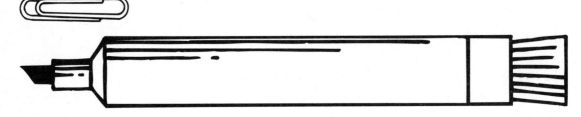

    Ⓐ about 1 inch   Ⓒ about 5 inches

    Ⓑ about 3 inches   Ⓓ about 7 inches

30. Rachel measures the height of her teacher's chair. Which is the best estimate for the height of the chair?

    Ⓕ about 1 yard   Ⓗ about 1 foot

    Ⓖ about 1 inch   Ⓙ Not Here

31. Mr. Tavla buys a new front door for his house. Which is the best estimate for the height of the door?

    Ⓐ about 1 centimeter   Ⓒ about 1 meter

    Ⓑ about 2 centimeters   Ⓓ about 2 meters

32. The bracelet is about 8 centimeters long. Which is the best estimate for the length of the stick?

F) about 1 centimeter

G) about 3 centimeters

H) about 6 centimeters

J) about 8 centimeters

---

33. Use the ruler below to measure the hair clip and the ribbon. How much longer is the ribbon than the hair clip?

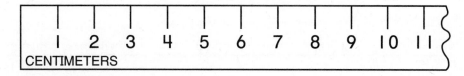

A) about 11 cm

B) about 8 cm

C) about 4 cm

D) about 3 cm

34. Use the ruler below to measure the ribbon and the crayon. How much longer is the ribbon than the crayon?

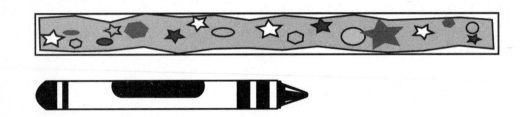

F) about 5 inches

G) about 4 inches

H) about 2 inches

J) about 1 inch

---

35. Sean wants to make a tile design that is 18 inches long and one that is 16 inches long. He draws a picture to help. How many inches of tiles will Sean need altogether?

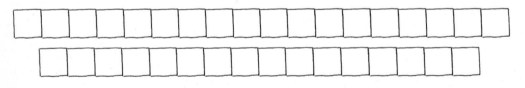

A) 34   B) 32   C) 24   D) 18

36. Erika buys 88 meters of fencing to make a place for her dog to play. She uses 70 meters of fencing and returns the rest to the store. How many meters of fencing does she return?

> 88 meters − 70 meters = □ meters

Ⓕ 81 meters   Ⓖ 28 meters   Ⓗ 20 meters   Ⓙ 18 meters

---

37. Manuel has 34 centimeters of orange ribbon and 29 centimeters of red ribbon. Which number sentence can he use to find the number of centimeters of ribbon altogether?

Ⓐ 34 cm + 29 cm = □ cm

Ⓑ 34 cm − □ cm = 29 cm

Ⓒ □ cm + 29 cm = 34 cm

Ⓓ 34 cm × 29 cm = □ cm

---

38. Wesley walks 57 yards from his house to Jamal's house. Then both of the boys walk 43 yards back toward Wesley's house. How far are they from Wesley's house?

> 57 yards − 43 yards = □ yards

Ⓕ 100 yards   Ⓖ 90 yards   Ⓗ 14 yards   Ⓙ 4 yards

39. Sam measures two sides of his garden. They are 13 feet long and 8 feet long. Sam shows the first number on a number line. If he adds the other number, where will he land on the number line?

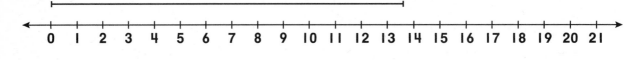

(A) 5   (B) 13   (C) 18   (D) Not Here

40. Sophia buys 18 meters of border trim to put around the top of a room. She uses 11 meters of the border trim. She uses a number line to show 18 meters. If she then subtracts 11 meters, where will she land on the number line?

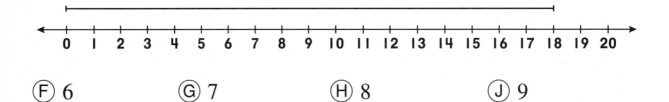

(F) 6   (G) 7   (H) 8   (J) 9

41. Carlton has pieces of string that are 55 inches long and 15 inches long. He uses a number line to add the lengths. First he draws a line from 0 to 55. If he then draws a line to show 15 more, where does he end on the number line?

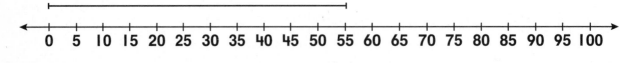

(A) 40   (B) 45   (C) 70   (D) 75

42. Gina has a rope that is 60 feet long. She cuts off 20 feet to make a long jump rope. She marks a number line to show 60 feet of rope. If she then draws a line backward by 20, where does she end on the number line?

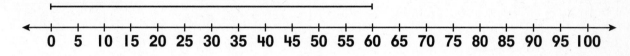

(F) 40   (G) 50   (H) 80   (J) Not Here

---

43. Which time is shown on the clock?

(A) 7:15   (B) 7:45   (C) 8:45   (D) 8:15

---

44. Which time is shown on the clock?

(F) 6:15   (G) 6:10   (H) 3:30   (J) 2:30

Measurement and Data
Higher Scores on Math, Grade 2

45. The time is after school and before bedtime. Which time is shown on the clock?

(A) 7:20 P.M.

(B) 7:20 A.M.

(C) 4:35 P.M.

(D) 4:35 A.M.

46. The Santos family is having breakfast. Which time is shown on their clock?

(F) 7:55 A.M.

(G) 7:05 P.M.

(H) 6:55 A.M.

(J) 6:55 P.M.

47. Ken has 4 dimes and 3 nickels. How much money does he have in all?

(A) 55¢

(B) 50¢

(C) 45¢

(D) 40¢

48. Shayla has 5 nickels and 6 pennies. How much money does she have in all?

(F) 11¢

(G) 31¢

(H) 36¢

(J) 56¢

Name _____ Date _____

49. The coins below show what Juan has in his piggy bank. How much money does Juan have in his piggy bank?

Ⓐ 25¢

Ⓑ 40¢

Ⓒ 45¢

Ⓓ 50¢

50. Mr. Li has these coins in his desk. What is the total value of his coins?

Ⓕ 17¢

Ⓖ 22¢

Ⓗ $17.00

Ⓙ $22.00

51. Alicia has money in her pocket that matches the picture. How much money does Alicia have in her pocket?

Ⓐ 1.75¢

Ⓑ $1.75

Ⓒ 1.50¢

Ⓓ $1.50

52. Use the ruler to measure the ribbons. Which line plot matches the data?

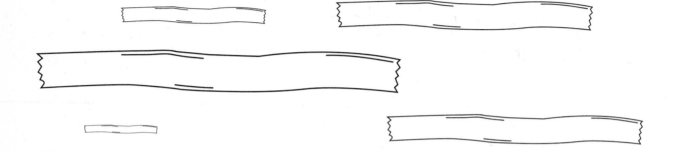

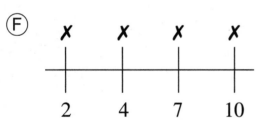
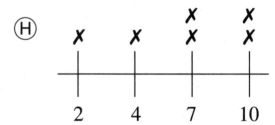
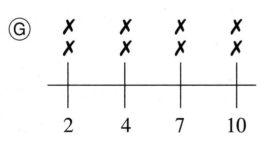
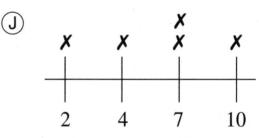

(F)

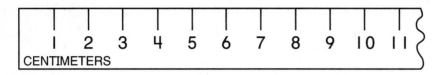

2   4   7   10

Lengths of Ribbons
in Centimeters

(H)

2   4   7   10

Lengths of Ribbons
in Centimeters

(G)

2   4   7   10

Lengths of Ribbons
in Centimeters

(J)

2   4   7   10

Lengths of Ribbons
in Centimeters

Name _____   Date _____

53. Jack measures the lengths of some boards. Use his list to complete the line plot. How many ✗s should be above the 12?

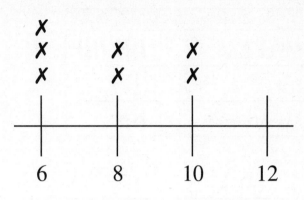

Lengths of Boards	
10 feet	8 feet
8 feet	6 feet
12 feet	10 feet
6 feet	6 feet

Lengths of Boards in Feet

(A) 0   (B) 1   (C) 7   (D) 8

---

54. Wendy measures the lengths of some ropes. Use her list to complete the line plot. How many ✗s should be above the 5?

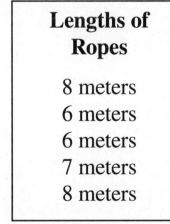

Lengths of Ropes

8 meters
6 meters
6 meters
7 meters
8 meters

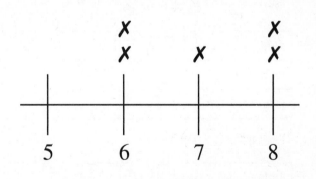

Lengths of Ropes in Meters

(F) 5   (G) 2   (H) 1   (J) 0

Name _____ Date _____

55. Ralph made a tally table to show some of the food at his family dinner. Which picture graph matches the table?

Food at Family Dinner		
Rolls	🥖	HHT IIIII
Pies	🥧	II
Sweet Potatoes	🥔	HHT

Ⓐ
Rolls	🍴 🍴 🍴 🍴 🍴 🍴 🍴 🍴 🍴
Pies	🍴 🍴
Sweet Potatoes	🍴 🍴 🍴 🍴 🍴

Key: Each 🍴 stands for 1.

Ⓑ
Rolls	🍴 🍴
Pies	🍴 🍴 🍴 🍴
Sweet Potatoes	🍴 🍴 🍴 🍴 🍴 🍴 🍴 🍴 🍴

Key: Each 🍴 stands for 1.

Ⓒ
Rolls	🍴 🍴 🍴 🍴 🍴 🍴 🍴 🍴 🍴
Pies	🍴 🍴 🍴 🍴
Sweet Potatoes	🍴

Key: Each 🍴 stands for 1.

Ⓓ
Rolls	🍴 🍴 🍴 🍴
Pies	🍴 🍴 🍴 🍴 🍴
Sweet Potatoes	🍴 🍴 🍴 🍴

Key: Each 🍴 stands for 1.

56. Look at the bar graph. How many apples and oranges are in the basket?

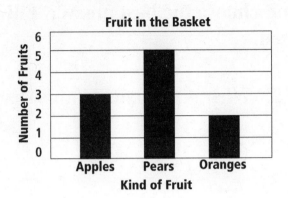

Fruit in the Basket

Number of Fruits

Apples   Pears   Oranges

Kind of Fruit

(F) 2

(G) 3

(H) 5

(J) 8

57. Look at the bar graph. Which hobby got the fewest votes for favorite?

Favorite Hobby

Hobby

Hiking
Reading
Music
Games

0   1   2   3   4   5

Number of Children

(A) hiking

(B) reading

(C) music

(D) games

Geometry

Modeled Instruction

DIRECTIONS: Read each question and choose the best answer. Fill in the circle for the answer you have chosen.

1. Which shape has only 3 angles?

Ⓐ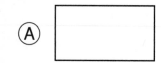

Ⓑ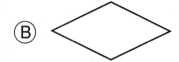

Ⓒ

Ⓓ

 **Hint**

Angles are sometimes called corners. A shape with 3 angles also has 3 sides.

2. What is the name of this shape?

Ⓕ hexagon

Ⓖ pentagon

Ⓗ rectangle

Ⓙ triangle

 Hint

The shape has 5 sides. The prefix *penta-* means 5. Choose the word that starts with *penta*.

3. Which shape is NOT a quadrilateral?

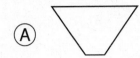
Ⓐ

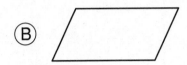
Ⓑ

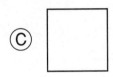
Ⓒ

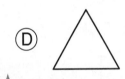
Ⓓ

 Hint

The prefix *quad-* means 4. All quadrilaterals have 4 sides. The sides do not have to be the same length. Choose the shape that does not have 4 sides.

4. Compare the square tile and the rectangle. How many tiles will cover the rectangle?

Ⓕ 2

Ⓖ 4

Ⓗ 8

Ⓙ 10

 Hint

The rectangle will hold 2 rows of tiles. There can be 4 tiles in each row. Add 4 + 4 to find the number of tiles in 2 rows.

5. The dot paper represents centimeter squares. How many centimeter squares will fit inside the rectangle?

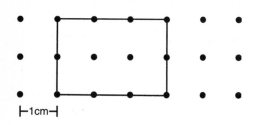

Ⓐ 3

Ⓑ 6

Ⓒ 4

Ⓓ 8

★ **Hint**

You can connect the dots to make centimeter squares inside the rectangle. Then there will be 2 rows of 3 squares. Add 3 + 3 to find the total number of squares that will fit.

6. Which figure does NOT show equal halves?

Ⓕ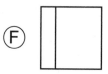

Ⓖ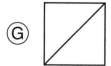

Ⓗ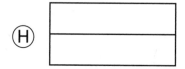

Ⓙ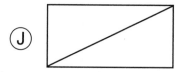

★ **Hint**

Each shape has a line that makes two parts, but one of the shapes does not show equal parts. A shape must have 2 equal parts to show halves.

7. Jacob draws a circle to show equal shares. He shades a fourth of the circle. Which figure shows what Jacob draws?

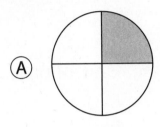
Ⓐ

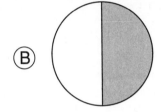
Ⓑ

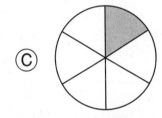
Ⓒ

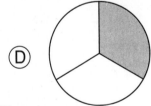
Ⓓ

 Hint

All of the circles show equal parts. There are 4 equal parts in fourths. Each part is called a fourth of the shape.

8. The rectangle has 3 equal shares. What is the name of the equal parts?

Ⓕ fourths

Ⓖ halves

Ⓗ fifths

Ⓙ thirds

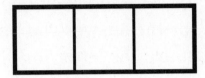 **Hint**

Equal parts can be named by the number of parts. For example, if there are 4 equal parts, the parts are named fourths. Choose the word that means 3 equal parts.

Geometry

Independent Practice

DIRECTIONS: Read each question and choose the best answer. Fill in the circle for the answer you have chosen. If the correct answer is not available, mark the letter for "Not Here."

9. Which shape has exactly 4 sides?

Ⓐ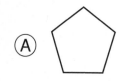

Ⓑ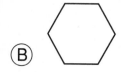

Ⓒ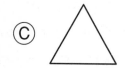

Ⓓ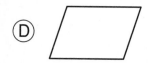

10. What is the name of this shape?

Ⓕ hexagon

Ⓖ pentagon

Ⓗ rectangle

Ⓙ triangle

Name _____   Date _____

11. How many angles are in this shape?

Ⓐ 2

Ⓑ 6

Ⓒ 8

Ⓓ 10

12. Which shape is NOT a triangle?

Ⓕ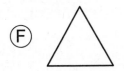

Ⓖ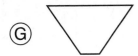

Ⓗ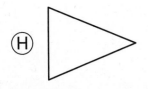

Ⓙ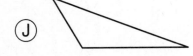

13. Which figure has a triangle inside a circle?

Ⓐ

Ⓑ

Ⓒ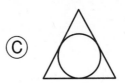

Ⓓ Not here

14. What is the name of this shape?

Ⓕ square

Ⓖ sphere

Ⓗ rectangle

Ⓙ cube

15. Helen draws a shape that has 0 angles and 0 sides. Which shape shows what Helen draws?

Ⓐ

Ⓑ

Ⓒ

Ⓓ

16. How many faces does this figure have?

Ⓕ 8

Ⓖ 6

Ⓗ 4

Ⓙ 3

17. Which is the name of this shape?

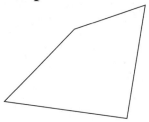

Ⓐ hexagon

Ⓑ octagon

Ⓒ quadrilateral

Ⓓ rectangle

18. Compare the square tile and the larger square. How many tiles will cover the larger square?

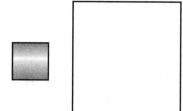

Ⓕ 12

Ⓖ 9

Ⓗ 6

Ⓙ 3

19. The dot paper represents centimeter squares. How many centimeter squares will fit inside the rectangle?

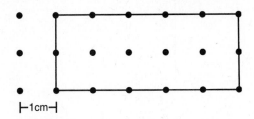

Ⓐ 12

Ⓑ 10

Ⓒ 8

Ⓓ 5

20. Look at the rectangle that is on grid paper. How many squares fit inside the rectangle?

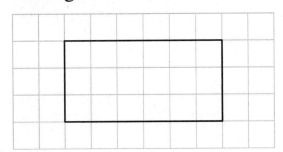

Ⓕ 6

Ⓖ 12

Ⓗ 15

Ⓙ 18

21. The dot paper represents centimeter squares. How many centimeter squares will fit inside the rectangle?

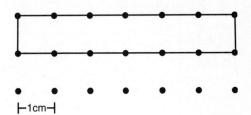

Ⓐ 6

Ⓑ 5

Ⓒ 4

Ⓓ 1

22. Look at the rectangle that is on grid paper. How many squares fit inside the rectangle?

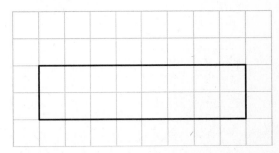

Ⓕ 16

Ⓖ 14

Ⓗ 12

Ⓙ 8

Name _____ Date _____

23. Compare the square tile and the larger square. How many tiles will cover the larger square?

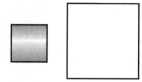

(A) 1

(B) 2

(C) 3

(D) 4

24. Which figure does NOT show equal shares?

(F)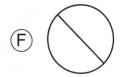

(G)

(H)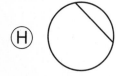

(J)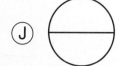

25. What part of the rectangle is shaded?

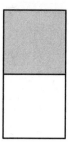

(A) a fourth of the shape

(B) a half of the shape

(C) a third of the shape

(D) Not Here

26. William cuts a sandwich into 4 equal shares. Which way can he describe the whole sandwich now?

(F) four fourths

(G) two fourths

(H) four halves

(J) two halves

Name _____ Date _____

27. Gracie draws a square to show equal parts. She shades a third of the square. Which figure shows what Gracie draws?

Ⓐ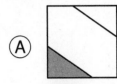

Ⓑ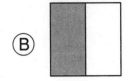

Ⓒ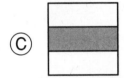

Ⓓ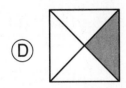

28. The circle has 6 equal parts. What is the name of the equal parts?

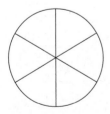

Ⓕ fourths

Ⓖ halves

Ⓗ thirds

Ⓙ Not Here

29. The circle shows 3 equal parts. All of the parts are shaded. Which words describe the shaded parts of the circle?

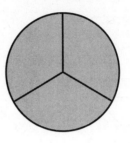

Ⓐ three thirds

Ⓑ four fourths

Ⓒ two halves

Ⓓ Not Here

30. Mr. Cobb cuts a sandwich into 2 equal parts. Which way can he describe the whole sandwich now?

Ⓕ two fourths

Ⓖ two halves

Ⓗ four fourths

Ⓙ four halves

Geometry
Higher Scores on Math, Grade 2

Name _____   Date _____

31. Which figure shows equal shares?

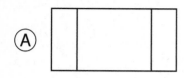

Ⓐ

Ⓑ

Ⓒ

Ⓓ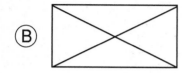

32. The circle has 2 equal parts. What is the name of the equal parts?

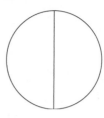

Ⓕ fourths

Ⓖ thirds

Ⓗ halves

Ⓙ Not Here

Name _____   Date _____

Practice Test A

DIRECTIONS: Read each question and choose the best answer. Fill in the circle for the answer you have chosen. If the correct answer is not available, mark the letter for "Not Here."

1. The circle has equal parts. What is the name of the equal parts?

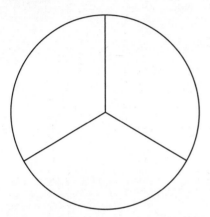

  Ⓐ thirds

  Ⓑ halves

  Ⓒ fourths

  Ⓓ Not Here

2. Larnell counts 5 baseballs and 10 soccer balls in the school gym. Then he counts 3 more baseballs. How many baseballs and soccer balls does Larnell count altogether?

  Ⓕ 12

  Ⓖ 15

  Ⓗ 18

  Ⓙ 20

3. Which number is forty-one?

  Ⓐ 401

  Ⓑ 104

  Ⓒ 41

  Ⓓ 14

4. Use mental math to subtract 704 − 100. What is the difference?

(F) 604   (G) 694   (H) 714   (J) 804

---

5. Use the inch ruler to measure. How long is the string?

0	I	2	3	4	5	6

inch

(A) 3 inches   (B) 4 inches   (C) 5 inches   (D) 6 inches

---

6. Tarika measures the lengths of some shoes. Use her list to complete the line plot. How many **✗**s should be above the 10?

Lengths of Shoes	
4 in.	7 in.
10 in.	8 in.
7 in.	10 in.
10 in.	4 in.

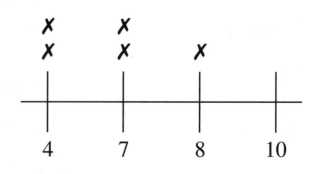

Lengths of Shoes in Inches

(F) 4   (G) 3   (H) 2   (J) 1

7. Gina buys 42 meters of red ribbon to decorate for a party. She also buys 36 meters of white ribbon. Which number sentence can she use to find the total length of the ribbons?

Ⓐ $42 - 36 = \square$ meters

Ⓑ $42 + \square = 36$ meters

Ⓒ $42 - 42 = \square$ meters

Ⓓ $42 + 36 = \square$ meters

8. Which figure does NOT show equal shares?

Ⓕ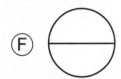

Ⓖ

Ⓗ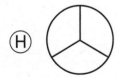

Ⓙ

9. There are 15 dogs in the park. There are 8 big dogs. The rest are small dogs. Which number sentence shows how to find the number of small dogs in the park?

Ⓐ $8 + \square = 15$

Ⓑ $8 - \square = 15$

Ⓒ $15 + 8 = \square$

Ⓓ $18 - 5 = \square$

10. What is the missing number?

$$\square + 5 = 12$$

Ⓕ 6   Ⓗ 8

Ⓖ 7   Ⓙ 9

11. Which number sentence does NOT equal 10?

Ⓐ $1 + 9 = \square$

Ⓑ $6 + 4 = \square$

Ⓒ $12 - 2 = \square$

Ⓓ $14 - 3 = \square$

Name _____   Date _____

12. Measure the nail in centimeters and in inches. About how long is the nail?

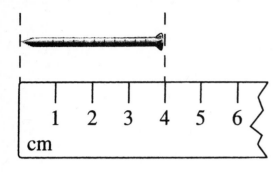

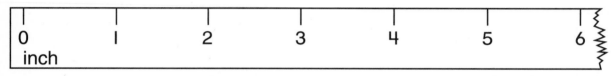

Ⓕ 4 inches, 4 centimeters

Ⓖ 4 inches, between 1 and 2 centimeters

Ⓗ 4 centimeters, between 2 and 3 inches

Ⓙ 4 centimeters, between 1 and 2 inches

_____

13. Which value is the same as nine hundred fifteen?

Ⓐ 951

Ⓑ 900 + 50

Ⓒ 900 + 10 + 5

Ⓓ 9 hundreds 15 tens

Practice Test A
Higher Scores on Math, Grade 2

14. Ahmed uses place-value blocks to add 164 + 117. Why does he rename 4 ones + 7 ones as 1 ten and 1 one?

(F) He has enough ones to regroup.

(G) He has enough tens to regroup.

(H) There are not enough tens to regroup.

(J) Not Here

15. Which number completes the number sentence?

$$52 + 17 = \square$$

(A) 79

(B) 69

(C) 65

(D) 35

16. Which pair of cube trains shows an even number?

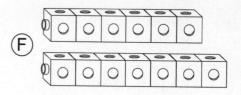

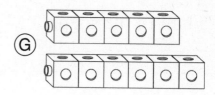

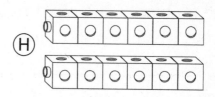

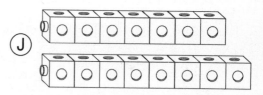

17. The time is shown on the clock. If it is near the end of Sam's school day, what time is it?

(A) 4:15 P.M.

(B) 4:15 A.M.

(C) 3:20 P.M.

(D) 3:20 A.M.

Name _____   Date _____

18. What part of the rectangle is shaded?

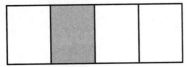

(F) a fourth of the shape   (H) a third of the shape

(G) a half of the shape   (J) Not Here

---

19. Use a place-value chart to add 521 + 297. Regroup ones or tens if you need to. What is the sum?

Hundreds	Tens	Ones
☐	☐	
5	2	1
+ 2	9	7

(A) 718   (B) 776   (C) 818   (D) 828

---

20. The bead is about 1 inch long. About how long is the whole string?

(F) about 2 inches   (H) about 6 inches

(G) about 4 inches   (J) about 8 inches

ЧMH Supplemental Publishers Inc.
Houghton Mifflin Harcourt Publishing Company

Practice Test A
Higher Scores on Math, Grade 2

21. Count by fives. What number comes next?

| 480, 485, 490, ☐ |

Ⓐ 491

Ⓑ 495

Ⓒ 500

Ⓓ 600

22. Compare the square tile and the rectangle. How many tiles will cover the rectangle?

Ⓕ 2

Ⓖ 4

Ⓗ 6

Ⓙ 9

23. Look at the bar graph. How many more children play soccer than baseball?

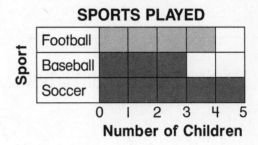

Ⓐ 12

Ⓑ 8

Ⓒ 3

Ⓓ 2

24. How many hundreds, tens, and ones are in 517?

Ⓕ 5 hundreds, 1 ten, 7 ones

Ⓖ 5 hundreds, 5 tens, 5 ones

Ⓗ 7 hundreds, 1 one, 7 tens

Ⓙ 7 hundreds, 1 ten, 5 ones

25. Sahib is 4 years older than Gavin. Jenny is 7 years older than Sahib. If Jenny is 13, how old is Gavin?

   Ⓐ 11   Ⓑ 9   Ⓒ 6   Ⓓ 2

---

26. Which row of butterflies shows an odd number?

Ⓕ

Ⓖ

Ⓗ

Ⓙ

---

27. Look at the place-value model. What value does it show?

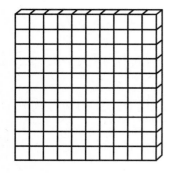 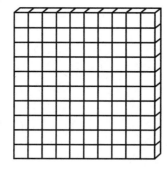

   Ⓐ 200   Ⓑ 20   Ⓒ 2 tens   Ⓓ 2 ones

28. June has 2 strings that are each 9 inches long. She marks the length of one string on a number line. If she adds the length of the other string, where will she land on the number line?

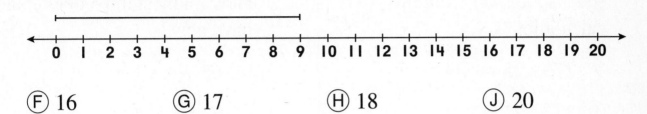

F) 16   G) 17   H) 18   J) 20

29. Luther has money in his desk that matches the picture. How much money does Luther have in his desk?

A) 45¢   B) $1.44   C) $1.45   D) 150¢

30. Which shape has 4 equal sides?

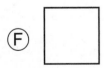

F)

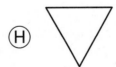

H)

G)

J)

Name _____   Date _____

31. Anya uses a calculator to subtract $52 - 25 = 27$. Which number sentence below can she also answer from this calculation?

Ⓐ $27 - 25 = \square$

Ⓑ $27 + 25 = \square$

Ⓒ $52 + 25 = \square$

Ⓓ $52 + 27 = \square$

32. Which number sentence shows how many squares are in this picture?

Ⓕ $5 + 5 = 10$

Ⓖ $5 + 5 + 5 = 15$

Ⓗ $5 + 5 + 5 + 5 = 20$

Ⓙ $5 + 5 + 5 + 5 + 5 = 25$

33. Zane has 72 stamps in his stamp collection. His friend gives him 4 more stamps. How many stamps does Zane have now?

Ⓐ 68

Ⓑ 72

Ⓒ 76

Ⓓ 78

34. Find the sum.

$$\begin{array}{r} \square \\ 27 \\ 22 \\ 15 \\ +\ 21 \\ \hline \end{array}$$

Ⓕ 95

Ⓖ 85

Ⓗ 75

Ⓙ 64

35. Which number makes both of these number sentences true?

$$8 + \square = 12$$
$$12 - 8 = \square$$

Ⓐ 3   Ⓑ 4   Ⓒ 5   Ⓓ 6

---

36. Some clocks have a round edge. Which is the best tool for measuring around the round edge of a clock?

Ⓕ centimeter ruler   Ⓗ meter stick

Ⓖ yardstick   Ⓙ measuring tape

---

37. Use the ruler below to measure the worm and the fly. How much longer is the worm than the fly?

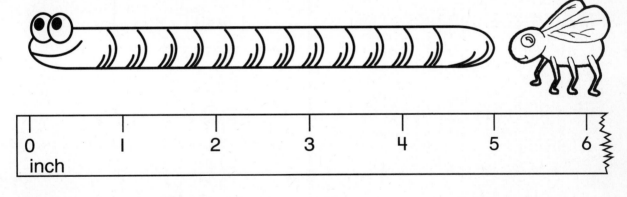

Ⓐ 4 in.   Ⓑ 3 in.   Ⓒ 2 in.   Ⓓ 1 in.

38. How many faces on this figure are rectangles?

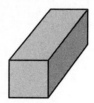

(F) 8

(G) 6

(H) 4

(J) 3

39. The model shows groups of 10 tens. Which statement does the model prove?

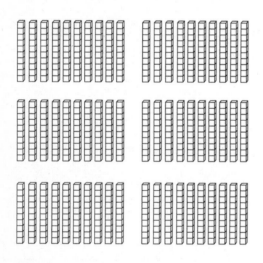

(A) 6 tens = 600

(B) 6 tens = 60 hundreds

(C) 60 tens = 60

(D) 60 tens = 6 hundreds

40. Which number sentence can you use to find the total number of bees?

(F) $2 + 2 + 2 = \square$

(G) $3 + 2 = \square$

(H) $3 + 3 + 3 = \square$

(J) $6 + 6 = \square$

41. Compare the numbers. Which symbol belongs in the box?

880 □ 808

(A) <

(B) =

(C) >

(D) Not Here

42. Chelsea has 3 quarters and 2 pennies. How much money does Chelsea have in all?

(F) 32¢

(G) 52¢

(H) 77¢

(J) 95¢

43. Ryan puts his books in 2 rows. There are 4 books in each row. Which addition sentence matches Ryan's books?

(A) 4 + 4 = 8

(B) 2 + 2 + 2 = 6

(C) 2 + 2 = 4

(D) Not Here

44. Which time is shown on the clock?

(F) 7:15

(G) 7:10

(H) 3:35

(J) 2:35

45. Find the difference.

$$\begin{array}{r} 7 \\ -\ 4 \\ \hline \end{array}$$

(A) 11

(B) 9

(C) 5

(D) Not Here

46. Meg places 13 feet of border along one side of her garden. She places 6 feet of border along another side. Use the number line. How many feet of border does Meg place in all?

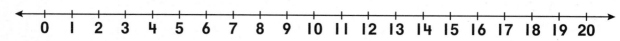

Ⓕ 13 feet   Ⓖ 19 feet   Ⓗ 21 feet   Ⓙ 26 feet

---

47. Find the sum.

$$30 + 27 + 20 = \square$$

Ⓐ 79   Ⓑ 77   Ⓒ 59   Ⓓ 57

---

48. Which is the name of this shape?

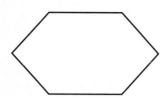

Ⓕ hexagon   Ⓖ pentagon   Ⓗ rectangle   Ⓙ triangle

Name _____   Date _____

49. The dot paper represents centimeter squares. How many centimeter squares will fit inside the rectangle?

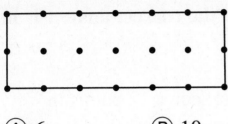

Ⓐ 6　　　　　Ⓑ 10　　　　　Ⓒ 12　　　　　Ⓓ 14

---

50. Which number sentence correctly describes this group of cats as an even number?

Ⓕ 8 = 4 + 4

Ⓖ 7 = 4 + 3

Ⓗ 5 = 2 + 2 + 1

Ⓙ 4 = 2 + 2

Name _____   Date _____

Practice Test B

DIRECTIONS: Read each question and choose the best answer. Fill in the circle for the answer you have chosen. If the correct answer is not available, mark the letter for "Not Here."

1. The rectangle has equal parts. What is the name of the equal parts?

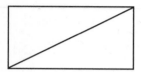

(A) fourths

(B) thirds

(C) halves

(D) Not Here

2. Tia scores 12 points in Monday's basketball game. She scores 26 points in Thursday's game. How many more points does Tia score on Thursday than on Monday?

(F) 12

(G) 14

(H) 34

(J) 38

3. Which number is fifty-six?

(A) 516

(B) 506

(C) 65

(D) 56

4. Use mental math to subtract 377 − 10. What is the difference?

(F) 387   (G) 376   (H) 367   (J) 277

---

5. Use the inch ruler to measure. How long is the straw?

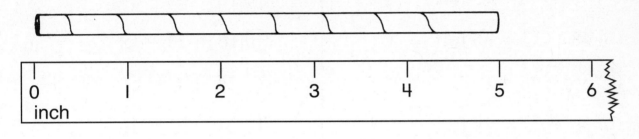

(A) 5 inches   (B) 4 inches   (C) 3 inches   (D) 2 inches

---

6. Logan measures the lengths of some spoons. Use his list to complete the line plot. How many ✗s should be above the 8?

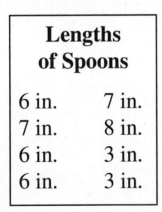

Lengths of Spoons	
6 in.	7 in.
7 in.	8 in.
6 in.	3 in.
6 in.	3 in.

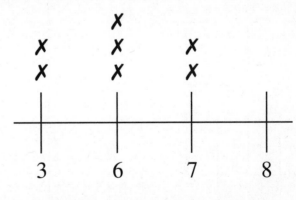

Lengths of Spoons in Inches

(F) 8   (G) 3   (H) 2   (J) 1

7. Aiden buys 48 feet of wood boards. He uses 36 feet of the wood boards to make a bench. Which number sentence can he use to find out how many feet of wood boards he has left?

Ⓐ $48 + 48 = \square$ feet

Ⓑ $48 - \square = 36$ feet

Ⓒ $36 + 48 = \square$ feet

Ⓓ $36 - \square = 48$ feet

8. Which figure does NOT show equal shares?

Ⓕ

Ⓖ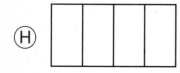

Ⓗ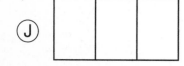

Ⓙ

9. Brooke plants 16 purple tulips in her garden. Then she plants 24 more tulips. Which number sentence shows how to find the total number of tulips that Brooke plants?

Ⓐ $16 + \square = 24$

Ⓑ $16 + 24 = \square$

Ⓒ $24 - 16 = \square$

Ⓓ $24 - \square = 16$

10. What is the missing number?

$$8 + \square = 10$$

Ⓕ 2

Ⓖ 4

Ⓗ 16

Ⓙ 18

Name _____ Date _____

11. Which number sentence does NOT equal 8?

(A) $4 + 4 = \square$

(B) $6 + 2 = \square$

(C) $14 - 7 = \square$

(D) $16 - 8 = \square$

12. Measure the leaf in centimeters and in inches. About how long is the leaf?

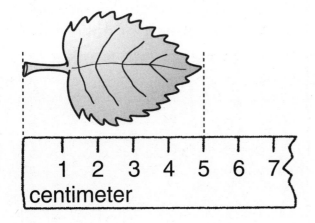

(F) about 5 centimeters, about 5 inches

(G) about 5 centimeters, about 2 inches

(H) about 2 centimeters, about 5 inches

(J) about 2 centimeters, about 2 inches

13. Which value is the same as six hundred thirty?

(A) 600 + 3

(B) 60 + 3

(C) 6 hundreds, 0 tens, 3 ones

(D) 6 hundreds, 3 tens, 0 ones

14. Ira uses place-value blocks to subtract 314 − 190. Why does he rename 314 as 2 hundreds, 11 tens, and 4 ones?

(F) There are too many hundreds.

(G) There are not enough ones to subtract.

(H) He cannot subtract 1 ten − 9 tens.

(J) Not Here

15. Which number completes the number sentence?

$$83 - 5 = \square$$

(A) 78

(B) 82

(C) 88

(D) 89

16. Which pair of cube trains shows an odd number?

(F)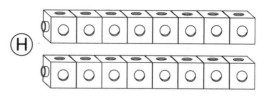

(G)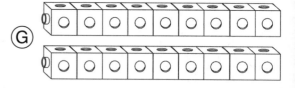

(H)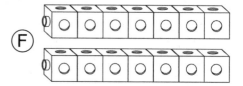

(J)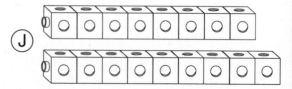

17. The time is shown on the clock. If it is almost time for the sun to rise, what time is it?

(A) 3:25 A.M.

(B) 3:25 P.M.

(C) 5:15 A.M.

(D) 5:15 P.M.

18. What part of the rectangle is shaded?

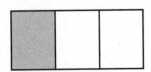

(F) a fourth of the shape

(G) a third of the shape

(H) a half of the shape

(J) Not Here

19. Use a place-value chart to add 452 + 129. Regroup ones or tens if you need to. What is the sum?

Hundreds	Tens	Ones
☐	☐	
4	5	2
+ 1	2	9

(A) 571

(B) 581

(C) 671

(D) 681

20. The bead is about 3 centimeters long. About how long is the whole string?

   Ⓕ about 3 cm

   Ⓖ about 6 cm

   Ⓗ about 9 cm

   Ⓙ about 12 cm

---

21. Count by hundreds. What number comes next?

> 700, 800, 900, □

Ⓐ 901   Ⓑ 905   Ⓒ 910   Ⓓ Not Here

---

22. Compare the square tile and the rectangle. How many tiles will cover the rectangle?

Ⓕ 10   Ⓖ 9   Ⓗ 6   Ⓙ 5

23. Look at the picture graph. How many blue whistles and green whistles are there altogether?

yellow							
blue							
green							

Each 🐚 stands for 1 whistle.

Ⓐ 10

Ⓑ 6

Ⓒ 4

Ⓓ 2

24. How many hundreds, tens, and ones are in 460?

Ⓕ 4 hundreds, 60 tens, 0 ones

Ⓖ 4 hundreds, 6 tens, 0 ones

Ⓗ 4 hundreds, 0 tens, 6 ones

Ⓙ 4 tens, 6 hundreds, 0 ones

25. Candace and Cameron are each 8 years old. Their older sister Carrie is 10 years old. What is the sum of all of their ages?

Ⓐ 2

Ⓑ 18

Ⓒ 26

Ⓓ 28

Name _____ Date _____

26. Which row of lizards shows an even number?

F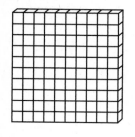

G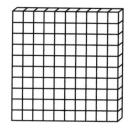

H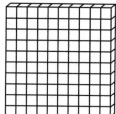

J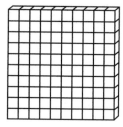

---

27. Look at the place-value model. What value does it show?

Ⓐ 40   Ⓑ 400   Ⓒ 4 tens   Ⓓ 4 ones

---

28. Habib has a board that is 16 feet long. He marks the length on a number line. He cuts 4 feet off the board. If he marks this on the number line, on what number will he land?

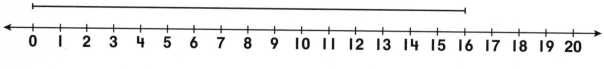

Ⓕ 12   Ⓖ 13   Ⓗ 19   Ⓙ 20

29. Beth has the coins that are in the picture. What is the total value of the coins?

- Ⓐ $62.00
- Ⓑ 62¢
- Ⓒ $67.00
- Ⓓ 67¢

30. Which shape has 4 sides?

Ⓕ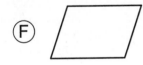

Ⓖ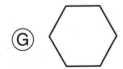

Ⓗ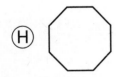

Ⓙ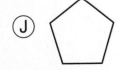

31. Miley uses a calculator to add $18 + 39 = 57$. Which number sentence below can she also answer from this calculation?

- Ⓐ $39 + 18 = \square$
- Ⓑ $39 - 18 = \square$
- Ⓒ $57 + 18 = \square$
- Ⓓ $57 + 39 = \square$

32. Which number sentence shows how many squares are in this picture?

☐ ☐ ☐
☐ ☐ ☐
☐ ☐ ☐
☐ ☐ ☐
☐ ☐ ☐

- Ⓕ $5 + 5 = 10$
- Ⓖ $3 + 3 + 3 + 3 = 12$
- Ⓗ $3 + 3 + 3 + 3 + 3 = 15$
- Ⓙ Not Here

33. There are 11 red grapes and 12 white grapes in a bowl. Celia eats 10 of the grapes. How many grapes are left?

(A) 33

(B) 23

(C) 22

(D) 13

34. Find the sum.

$$\begin{array}{r} \square \\ 17 \\ 13 \\ 11 \\ +\ 16 \\ \hline \end{array}$$

(F) 46

(G) 47

(H) 57

(J) 58

35. Which number makes both of these number sentences true?

$$6 + \square = 15$$
$$15 - 6 = \square$$

(A) 9

(B) 8

(C) 7

(D) 6

36. Some bookmarks are about the length of a book. Which is the best tool for measuring the length of a bookmark?

(F) inch ruler

(G) measuring tape

(H) meter stick

(J) yardstick

Name _____   Date _____

37. Use the ruler below to measure the fork and the knife. How much longer is the knife than the fork?

(A) 3 in.   (B) 2 in.   (C) 1 in.   (D) 0 in.

---

38. How many square faces are there on this figure?

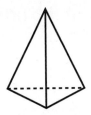

(F) 6   (G) 4   (H) 3   (J) 0

39. The model shows groups of 10 tens. Which statement does the model prove?

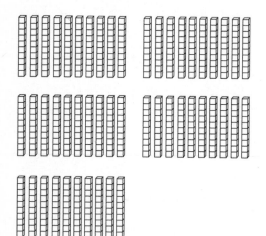

  Ⓐ 50 tens = 50

  Ⓑ 50 tens = 5 hundreds

  Ⓒ 5 tens = 500

  Ⓓ 5 tens = 50 hundreds

40. Which number sentence can you use to find the total number of worms?

  Ⓕ $4 + 4 + 4 = \square$

  Ⓖ $4 + 4 + 4 + 4 = \square$

  Ⓗ $5 + 5 + 5 + 5 = \square$

  Ⓙ $5 + 5 + 5 + 5 + 5 = \square$

41. Compare the numbers. Which symbol belongs in the box?

$$555 \,\square\, 556$$

  Ⓐ >

  Ⓑ =

  Ⓒ <

  Ⓓ Not Here

42. Lucy has 1 dollar bill, 2 dimes, and 2 nickels. How much money does Lucy have in all?

Ⓕ $1.30

Ⓖ $1.22

Ⓗ 120¢

Ⓙ 112¢

43. Chet puts his crackers in 2 rows. There are 5 crackers in each row. Which number sentence shows how many crackers Chet has in all?

Ⓐ 5 + 5 + 5 = 15

Ⓑ 5 + 5 = 10

Ⓒ 2 + 2 + 2 + 2 = 8

Ⓓ 2 + 2 + 2 = 6

44. Which time is shown on the clock?

Ⓕ 3:15

Ⓖ 3:20

Ⓗ 4:15

Ⓙ 4:20

45. Find the difference.

$$\begin{array}{r} 9 \\ -\ 7 \\ \hline \end{array}$$

Ⓐ 2

Ⓑ 3

Ⓒ 16

Ⓓ Not Here

Name _____ Date _____

46. Myra has a rope that is 20 feet long. She cuts 12 feet off the rope. Use the number line. How long is the rope after she cuts off 12 feet?

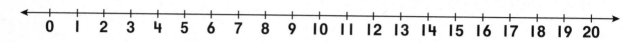

Ⓕ 18 feet   Ⓖ 9 feet   Ⓗ 8 feet   Ⓙ 6 feet

47. Find the sum.

$$11 + 12 + 33 = \square$$

Ⓐ 44   Ⓑ 45   Ⓒ 46   Ⓓ 56

48. Which is the name of this shape?

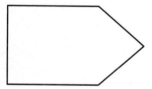

Ⓕ hexagon   Ⓖ quadrilateral   Ⓗ rectangle   Ⓙ pentagon

49. The dot paper represents centimeter squares. How many centimeter squares will fit inside the rectangle?

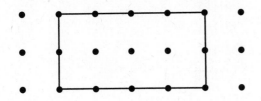

(A) 10

(B) 8

(C) 4

(D) 2

50. Which number sentence correctly describes this group of bees as an odd number?

(F) $10 = 5 + 5$

(G) $9 = 4 + 4 + 1$

(H) $8 = 4 + 4$

(J) $7 = 3 + 3 + 1$

Practice Test B
Higher Scores on Math, Grade 2

Answer Key

Pretest

1. A [2.OA.1]
2. J [2.OA.1]
3. B [2.OA.1]
4. H [2.OA.1]
5. C [2.OA.2]
6. G [2.OA.2]
7. D [2.OA.2]
8. F [2.OA.2]
9. B [2.OA.3]
10. J [2.OA.3]
11. A [2.OA.3]
12. H [2.OA.4]
13. C [2.OA.4]
14. G [2.OA.4]
15. D [2.NBT.1]
16. F [2.NBT.1.a]
17. D [2.NBT.1.b]
18. H [2.NBT.2]
19. B [2.NBT.3]
20. G [2.NBT.3]
21. C [2.NBT.4]
22. J [2.NBT.5]
23. A [2.NBT.5]
24. F [2.NBT.6]
25. D [2.NBT.6]
26. H [2.NBT.7]
27. C [2.NBT.8]
28. G [2.NBT.9]
29. A [2.MD.1]
30. J [2.MD.1]
31. B [2.MD.2]
32. F [2.MD.3]
33. B [2.MD.4]
34. G [2.MD.5]
35. A [2.MD.5]
36. J [2.MD.6]
37. D [2.MD.7]
38. H [2.MD.7]
39. C [2.MD.8]
40. F [2.MD.8]
41. A [2.MD.9]
42. H [2.MD.10]
43. D [2.G.1]
44. G [2.G.1]
45. C [2.G.1]
46. J [2.G.2]
47. B [2.G.2]
48. F [2.G.3]
49. C [2.G.3]
50. H [2.G.3]

Operations and Algebraic Thinking
Modeled Instruction

1. C [2.OA.1]
2. F [2.OA.1]
3. D [2.OA.1]
4. G [2.OA.1]
5. A [2.OA.1]
6. H [2.OA.1]
7. C [2.OA.1]
8. J [2.OA.1]
9. B [2.OA.1]
10. G [2.OA.1]
11. B [2.OA.2]
12. J [2.OA.2]
13. A [2.OA.2]
14. H [2.OA.2]
15. D [2.OA.2]
16. F [2.OA.2]

Answer Key
Higher Scores on Math, Grade 2

17. D [2.OA.3]

18. F [2.OA.3]

19. A [2.OA.3]

20. H [2.OA.3]

21. C [2.OA.3]

22. G [2.OA.4]

23. D [2.OA.4]

24. G [2.OA.4]

Operations and Algebraic Thinking
Independent Practice

25. A [2.OA.1]

26. G [2.OA.1]

27. D [2.OA.1]

28. J [2.OA.1]

29. B [2.OA.1]

30. H [2.OA.1]

31. C [2.OA.1]

32. F [2.OA.1]

33. D [2.OA.1]

34. H [2.OA.1]

35. B [2.OA.1]

36. F [2.OA.1]

37. C [2.OA.1]

38. G [2.OA.1]

39. A [2.OA.1]

40. J [2.OA.1]

41. B [2.OA.1]

42. J [2.OA.1]

43. A [2.OA.1]

44. F [2.OA.1]

45. D [2.OA.1]

46. H [2.OA.1]

47. C [2.OA.2]

48. G [2.OA.2]

49. C [2.OA.2]

50. G [2.OA.2]

51. D [2.OA.2]

52. H [2.OA.2]

53. A [2.OA.2]

54. J [2.OA.2]

55. B [2.OA.2]

56. F [2.OA.2]

57. D [2.OA.2]

58. H [2.OA.2]

59. C [2.OA.2]

60. J [2.OA.2]

61. B [2.OA.3]

62. G [2.OA.3]

63. A [2.OA.3]

64. J [2.OA.3]

65. B [2.OA.3]

66. H [2.OA.3]

67. A [2.OA.3]

68. F [2.OA.3]

69. D [2.OA.3]

70. J [2.OA.3]

71. C [2.OA.4]

72. G [2.OA.4]

73. D [2.OA.4]

74. H [2.OA.4]

75. C [2.OA.4]

76. J [2.OA.4]

77. B [2.OA.4]

78. F [2.OA.4]

Number and Operations in Base Ten
Modeled Instruction

1. C [2.NBT.1]

2. G [2.NBT.1]

3. D [2.NBT.1.a]

4. F [2.NBT.1.b]

5. B [2.NBT.2]

6. H [2.NBT.2]

7. A [2.NBT.3]

8. J [2.NBT.3]

9. A [2.NBT.4]

10. H [2.NBT.4]

11. C [2.NBT.5]

12. G [2.NBT.5]

13. B [2.NBT.5]

14. J [2.NBT.6]

15. D [2.NBT.6]

16. F [2.NBT.7]

17. C [2.NBT.7]

18. J [2.NBT.8]

19. B [2.NBT.8]

20. F [2.NBT.9]

Number and Operations in Base Ten

Independent Practice

21. B [2.NBT.1]

22. J [2.NBT.1]

23. A [2.NBT.1]

24. H [2.NBT.1]

25. D [2.NBT.1.a]

26. G [2.NBT.1.a]

27. C [2.NBT.1.b]

28. F [2.NBT.1.b]

29. B [2.NBT.2]

30. J [2.NBT.2]

31. A [2.NBT.2]

32. G [2.NBT.2]

33. C [2.NBT.3]

34. F [2.NBT.3]

35. D [2.NBT.3]

36. H [2.NBT.3]

37. C [2.NBT.4]

38. G [2.NBT.4]

39. A [2.NBT.4]

40. H [2.NBT.4]

41. B [2.NBT.5]

42. J [2.NBT.5]

43. D [2.NBT.5]

44. F [2.NBT.5]

45. A [2.NBT.5]

46. H [2.NBT.5]

47. B [2.NBT.5]

48. J [2.NBT.6]

49. C [2.NBT.6]

50. G [2.NBT.6]

51. D [2.NBT.6]

52. F [2.NBT.7]

53. C [2.NBT.7]

54. F [2.NBT.7]

55. D [2.NBT.7]

56. G [2.NBT.7]

57. A [2.NBT.7]

58. J [2.NBT.8]

59. B [2.NBT.8]

60. H [2.NBT.8]

61. C [2.NBT.9]

62. G [2.NBT.9]

Measurement and Data

Modeled Instruction

1. D [2.MD.1]

2. G [2.MD.1]

3. B [2.MD.2]

4. J [2.MD.2]

5. C [2.MD.3]

6. F [2.MD.3]

7. A [2.MD.4]

8. H [2.MD.5]

9. B [2.MD.5]

10. J [2.MD.6]

11. B [2.MD.6]

12. H [2.MD.7]

13. D [2.MD.7]

14. F [2.MD.8]

15. C [2.MD.8]

16. G [2.MD.9]

17. B [2.MD.9]

18. H [2.MD.10]

19. A [2.MD.10]

20. G [2.MD.10]

Measurement and Data

Independent Practice

21. C [2.MD.1]

22. F [2.MD.1]

23. D [2.MD.1]

24. G [2.MD.1]

25. A [2.MD.1]

26. J [2.MD.2]

27. B [2.MD.2]

28. H [2.MD.2]

29. C [2.MD.3]

30. F [2.MD.3]

31. D [2.MD.3]

32. G [2.MD.3]

33. B [2.MD.4]

34. H [2.MD.4]

35. A [2.MD.5]

36. J [2.MD.5]

37. A [2.MD.5]

38. H [2.MD.5]

39. D [2.MD.6]

40. G [2.MD.6]

41. C [2.MD.6]

42. F [2.MD.6]

43. B [2.MD.7]

44. J [2.MD.7]

45. C [2.MD.7]

46. H [2.MD.7]

47. A [2.MD.8]

48. G [2.MD.8]

49. D [2.MD.8]

50. F [2.MD.8]

51. B [2.MD.8]

52. J [2.MD.9]

53. B [2.MD.9]

54. J [2.MD.9]

55. A [2.MD.10]

56. H [2.MD.10]

57. D [2.MD.10]

Geometry

Modeled Instruction

1. C [2.G.1]

2. G [2.G.1]

3. D [2.G.1]

4. H [2.G.2]

5. B [2.G.2]

6. F [2.G.3]

7. A [2.G.3]

8. J [2.G.3]

Geometry

Independent Practice

9. D [2.G.1]

10. F [2.G.1]

11. C [2.G.1]

12. G [2.G.1]

13. A [2.G.1]

14. J [2.G.1]

15. B [2.G.1]

16. G [2.G.1]

17. C [2.G.1]

18. G [2.G.2]

19. B [2.G.2]

20. J [2.G.2]

21. A [2.G.2]

22. F [2.G.2]

23. D [2.G.2]

24. H [2.G.3]

25. B [2.G.3]

26. F [2.G.3]

27. C [2.G.3]

28. J [2.G.3]

29. A [2.G.3]

30. G [2.G.3]

31. D [2.G.3]

32. H [2.G.3]

Answer Key

Higher Scores on Math, Grade 2

Practice Test A

1. A [2.G.3]
2. H [2.OA.1]
3. C [2.NBT.3]
4. F [2.NBT.8]
5. B [2.MD.1]
6. G [2.MD.9]
7. D [2.MD.5]
8. J [2.G.3]
9. A [2.OA.1]
10. G [2.OA.2]
11. D [2.OA.2]
12. J [2.MD.2]
13. C [2.NBT.3]
14. F [2.NBT.9]
15. B [2.NBT.5]
16. H [2.OA.3]
17. A [2.MD.7]
18. F [2.G.3]
19. C [2.NBT.7]
20. G [2.MD.3]
21. B [2.NBT.2]
22. H [2.G.2]
23. D [2.MD.10]
24. F [2.NBT.1]
25. D [2.OA.1]
26. G [2.OA.3]
27. A [2.NBT.1.b]
28. H [2.MD.6]
29. C [2.MD.8]
30. F [2.G.1]
31. B [2.NBT.5]
32. G [2.OA.4]
33. C [2.OA.1]
34. G [2.NBT.6]
35. B [2.OA.2]
36. J [2.MD.1]
37. A [2.MD.4]
38. H [2.G.1]

39. D [2.NBT.1.a]
40. F [2.OA.4]
41. C [2.NBT.4]
42. H [2.MD.8]
43. A [2.OA.4]
44. J [2.MD.7]
45. D [2.OA.2]
46. G [2.MD.5]
47. B [2.NBT.6]
48. F [2.G.1]
49. C [2.G.2]
50. J [2.OA.3]

Practice Test B

1. C [2.G.3]
2. G [2.OA.1]
3. D [2.NBT.3]
4. H [2.NBT.8]
5. A [2.MD.1]
6. J [2.MD.9]
7. B [2.MD.5]
8. F [2.G.3]
9. B [2.OA.1]
10. F [2.OA.2]
11. C [2.OA.2]
12. G [2.MD.2]
13. D [2.NBT.3]
14. H [2.NBT.9]
15. A [2.NBT.5]
16. J [2.OA.3]
17. C [2.MD.7]
18. G [2.G.3]
19. B [2.NBT.7]
20. H [2.MD.3]
21. D [2.NBT.2]
22. F [2.G.2]
23. A [2.MD.10]
24. G [2.NBT.1]
25. C [2.OA.1]

Answer Key
Higher Scores on Math, Grade 2

26. J [2.OA.3]

27. B [2.NBT.1.b]

28. F [2.MD.6]

29. D [2.MD.8]

30. F [2.G.1]

31. A [2.NBT.5]

32. H [2.OA.4]

33. D [2.OA.1]

34. H [2.NBT.6]

35. A [2.OA.2]

36. F [2.MD.1]

37. C [2.MD.4]

38. J [2.G.1]

39. B [2.NBT.1.a]

40. G [2.OA.4]

41. C [2.NBT.4]

42. F [2.MD.8]

43. B [2.OA.4]

44. G [2.MD.7]

45. A [2.OA.2]

46. H [2.MD.5]

47. D [2.NBT.6]

48. J [2.G.1]

49. B [2.G.2]

50. G [2.OA.3]

Reference Sheet

Symbols

=	<	>
equals 4 = 4	is less than 5 < 6	is greater than 6 > 5

Number Models

1 hundred = 100	1 ten = 10	1 one = 1

Coins

penny 1¢	nickel 5¢	dime 10¢	quarter 25¢

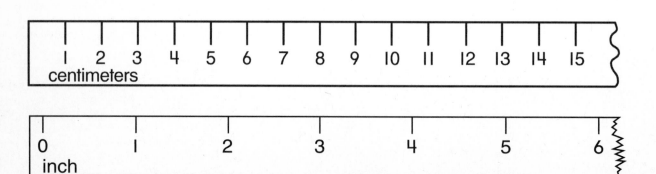

Shapes

Triangles	Quadrilaterals	Pentagons	Hexagons
3 sides 3 angles	4 sides 4 angles	5 sides 5 angles	6 sides 6 angles

Special Quadrilaterals

Squares	Rectangles
4 equal sides 4 equal angles	2 pairs of sides equal 4 equal angles